$10 \frac{00}{}$

BRIDE OF GLORY

BRIDE OF GLORY

The Story of Elizabeth Bacon Custer

BY MARGARET LEIGHTON

ARIEL BOOKS

FARRAR, STRAUS AND CUDAHY

NEW YORK

To Dr. Lawrence Frost
of Monroe Michigan
with gratitude and regard

Ariel Books
a division of
Farrar, Straus and Cudahy

Published simultaneously in Canada by
Ambassador Books, Ltd., Toronto

Manufactured in the U.S.A.

CHAPTER

1

Libbie Bacon was swinging. The swing was new; only this morning she had watched her father and Abner, the hired man, sink the tall upright poles firmly in the earth, fasten the cross-beam and thread the ropes through holes bored in a smooth-planed seat.

It was very high, the highest swing ten-year-old Libbie had ever seen. She had felt a little twinge of fear when she first settled herself on the seat, grasped the stiff, new-smelling ropes with both her hands, and looked up at their enormous length stretched so far above her. But all spring she had begged and teased Judge Bacon, her father, to make her the highest swing in all Monroe, Michigan. Now that it was hers she would rather die than show her fear.

"All ready, daughter?" the Judge asked, pulling her backwards as far as the ropes would reach.

"Ready, set and go!" she cried. He gave her a powerful push and sent her swooping forward.

With the first soaring rush through the air, her fears vanished in pure, breathless joy. That had been early this morning, and now, although it was almost noon, she was still swinging. Back and forth, back and forth, while the wind blew her bright chestnut curls first forward against her cheeks, then backwards away from her face. With her brown calico frock, her starched white petticoats and even the ruffles of her long pantalettes fluttering and flying, she pumped at the ropes, heedless of the blisters that were forming on her palms. Up, up, up, pausing for a heart-stopping moment so high that she could see the tops of all the blossoming fruit trees in the yard, over parts of the house-roof she had never glimpsed before and even into the swallows' nests along the barn eaves, then back and down again with thrilling speed. At the top of each swing she leaned back, straight-armed, and stretched out her toes until her cross-strapped slippers were black against the blue sky and pulled and pumped herself ever higher and higher.

The air felt smooth and solid against her face, like cold flowing water. This is the way birds feel, she told herself, or maybe fish in the river. Yes, and horses, too, galloping over level turf as fast as they can go. She shut her eyes, imagining herself a soaring bird, a fish or a horse with mane streaming in the wind.

In a window of the house Judge Bacon and Sophia, his wife, stood together watching their daughter. "*Who* was saying, only last week, that *I* indulged our little girl when I bought her the piano for her birthday?" Sophia Bacon asked fondly.

The Judge smiled and shook his head. "This was only one morning's work for me. Her piano cost you far more. Confess that it was only to save money to buy it that you took over the work of bookkeeper for me."

"That's true," she admitted. "But oh, Daniel, I have such hopes for her. I want to give her every accomplishment and advantage a girl can have." He started to speak, but she continued. "Wait—I know what you are thinking. *Of course,* above all, my greatest prayer is that she grow up in the fear of the Lord, to be a good and pious woman. But for now, Daniel, I do want her to be a happy child."

"I never knew a happier, healthier child," he told her. Then for a moment both were silent, thinking of three small graves in the shaded graveyard not far away. Two tiny daughters had died in infancy and later a fine, promising little boy. Libbie was now their only child. They were no longer young and all their devotion was centered on her.

"She has been swinging so long. Won't she tire herself?" Sophia asked, after an interval. "Perhaps I should call her in for a rest."

"No, let her alone for a little while more," he answered. "After all, her swing is only new once. Besides, I think that the news of it has spread. Here come her playmates. She won't have it to herself much longer."

The rhythmic squeaking of the swing slowed and stopped as Libbie caught sight of the group of boys and girls pouring through the gate in the picket fence. She slipped off the seat and stood clinging to the ropes, proud but a little dizzy from the long motion. "Fanny, Kate, Laura, Arthur, Fred! Everybody! Come and try my new swing. Pa just put it up this morning. Isn't it the highest you ever saw?"

For the rest of the morning Libbie was content to give up her swing to her playmates, partly because she was naturally sociable and generous and partly because her blistered palms had begun to sting.

"Your Pa is surely a good swing-builder," Fred stated. He and Libbie sat perched each on one of the square-topped posts of the fence while he waited his turn. "Oh Libbie! Look there across the street. There's poor old Pierre."

Libbie looked and her bright smile faded. An old man was

shuffling along the sidewalk in the thin, dappled shade of the spring leaves. The hat pulled down over his face did not hide the terrible, livid scars that marred it. "Yes, I know," she said. "He comes by just at this time every day to get his mail down at the post office. It scares me even to look at him, but Ma says it's good for us to be reminded of what people had to go through in the old days. To remember that there were once dangerous wild Indians right here in Monroe."

"It wasn't Monroe then," Fred corrected importantly.

"*I* know that," Libbie told him, making a little face. "Last term at the Seminary we studied history and we learned *all* about the War of 1812 and the Battle of Raisin River with the British, and the Indian massacre afterwards, all right here in our own town. All of us had nightmares for a week! I still have them, once in a while, after I've seen old Pierre and think of how he went through it all and was so horribly tortured."

"That's because you're a girl," Fred stated. "My father says that the Reverend Boyd is much too advanced in his Seminary. He teaches girls things that females shouldn't try to learn. Their brains aren't made for hard study."

Libbie gave a gasp of indignation and was about to answer when Freddy interrupted. "Hello, Autie!" he called out.

Libbie turned again to see an older boy with a strapful of books over his shoulder coming along under the arch of trees. He was whistling a lively tune in time to his rapid stride, but he stopped his whistling, grinned in a friendly fashion, and waved his hand in answer. "Hello there, Freddy," he called. The sunlight filtered down through the branches and gleamed briefly on a thatch of curly yellow hair and his eyes were the bluest Libbie had ever seen.

"Who was that?" she asked as soon as he had passed.

"That's Autie Custer," Fred told her. "He's come here

from Ohio to go to school at Stebbins Academy. He lives
with his sister, Mrs. Reed, down the street there. My big
brother knows him at school and he says he's the strongest
boy there. He says that he's planning to go to West Point."

"West Point? Where is that?" Libbie asked.

Freddy stared at her. "Don't you know? Why, West Point
is where young men go to learn how to be army officers—
captains and majors and colonels and generals." His voice was
scornful. "I thought everybody, even girls, knew that!"

Libbie tossed her head. "Pooh, who cares about army officers? Judges are lots more important and *my* pa's a judge!"
Nevertheless she leaned out over the fence and watched the
yellow-haired boy disappearing down the street until the
sound of his whistling faded away. "What a funny name,
'Autie'!" she added.

"That's just a nickname. His real name's Armstrong—George
Armstrong Custer," Freddy explained. "Ah, it's my turn at
last!" and he jumped down and raced toward the swing.

Almost a week later Libbie and Laura Noble, just returned
from school, were swinging on her gate waiting for some of
their friends to join them when the tall young scholar came
past again. "Who is that big boy?" Laura asked. "I think he's
handsome!"

"*I* know who he is," Libbie told her. "That's Autie Custer.
He goes to Stebbins Academy. He lives just down the street."

"Then why don't you speak to him if you know him?"
Laura asked.

"Well, I don't *really* know him. We haven't been introduced," Libbie admitted. "I only know who he is."

"Go ahead, speak to him anyway. I dare you to," Laura
whispered.

Speaking to a boy who hadn't been formally introduced was

against all the strict rules of Libbie's upbringing. It was even "unladylike," and to be thought "unladylike" was a dreadful fate. But a dare was a dare. Libbie drew in her breath. "Hello there, you Custer boy!" she called out. Then, suddenly appalled by her boldness, she jumped off the gate and ran up the walk to the house in a swirl of petticoats.

From the safety of the porch Libbie gave a frightened look over her shoulder before she entered the house. The Custer boy was laughing! He waved his hand to her and she saw again how startlingly blue his eyes were in his sunburnt face.

"Oh Libbie, you did it! You spoke to a strange boy!" Laura giggled. "I never thought you really would, Libbie Bacon!"

"Well, what did you dare me to for?" Libbie demanded. "It wasn't my fault. I had to take your dare."

There was a rustle of skirts on the stairs and Mrs. Bacon appeared in the hall. Oh heavens, did Ma hear me? Libbie thought in a panic. But her mother's face was serene and smiling.

"Is that you, Libbie? Good afternoon, Laura," she said. "Libbie, what do you think? A letter came today from your aunt in Grand Rapids. They hope that we will make them a visit as soon as your school is out, and your father says that we may."

"We're going to Grand Rapids!" Libbie cried, clapping her hands and twirling around with pleasure. There was no place Libbie, an only child, liked better than that house filled with lively cousins. "Oh Laura, it's such fun there! I can hardly wait until school's out." What a relief, too, to know that her mother had not seen nor heard her bold improper act!

That evening at supper Libbie spoke up as casually as she could. "Do you know Mrs. Reed who lives down the block?" she asked her mother.

"No, but I know who she is," Sophia Bacon answered. "She belongs to the Methodist Church, I believe. Her husband is a drayman, isn't he, Daniel?"

The Judge nodded. "Yes, an honest, hard-working fellow, but a Democrat, I'm afraid."

"Did you meet her somewhere, Libbie?" Mrs. Bacon asked.

"Oh no," Libbie answered quickly. "I just wondered." Inwardly she breathed a sigh of relief. If Ma doesn't know Mrs. Reed, there's no chance of her finding out what I did, she thought, comforted.

Monroe was a small town in 1852, but it was divided, nevertheless, into strict social classes. The Reeds and the Custers were Methodists and Democrats, the Bacons were Republicans and Presbyterians. David Reed, Autie's brother-in-law, was doing well at his draying business, but he was still rated a "working man." Judge Bacon was one of the town's wealthiest and most respected citizens. The paths of the two families simply never crossed, and Autie Custer's name did not appear anywhere in the diary Libbie soon began to keep.

There was much else to record and she set it down with a lively, dramatic style all her own. School days at the Boyd Seminary for girls which her father had helped to found were busy and absorbing. There were piano lessons, too, as well as church and Sabbath school to attend. That year she spent long hours sitting for an oil portrait in her best off-shoulder white dress, pink coral necklace and bracelet, with her hair carefully smoothed on top and curled at the sides.

There were many sewing and knitting stints to be accomplished and then recorded in Libbie's diary. One day came news that a "dissipated German living near the depot" had committed suicide, setting the town agog. Another day the lamp in the hall "fell and broke of itself," miraculously not burning down the house. "We went to hear some 'spiritual knockings' last evening at Fanny's" she wrote down. "Pa says they were humbugs, but I don't see how he could know." Bible chapters learned systematically by heart were part of her record of events and then, on a following page, came an account of how strangely bright the moon had been that night and how it had brought out "young gentlemen and ladies walking together past the house and down towards the river." Another entry read, "My mother read a religious tract to me today, all about the awful 'Day of Trial.' I certainly hope I don't turn out to be a sinner!" But almost on the same page she put down a description of her new spring bonnet of straw trimmed with "elegant purple velvet pansies made in France and tied with real silk ribbons."

Most enthusiastic of all were the accounts of trips not only to Grand Rapids, but also to her father's relatives in New York State. In the summer they traveled by rail and stagecoach, but in winter by sleigh, bundled in buffalo robes, and speeding through the frosty countryside where the glimpsed lakes seemed a darker blue than ever in contrast to the snow's dazzling whiteness. Both families were large and hospitable and Libbie adored the company of her many gay and friendly cousins.

The next two years went smoothly and happily, for Libbie was too young to read the meaning in her mother's growing weakness or the deepened furrows in Judge Bacon's face. Not until the doctor began to come almost every day and her mother's sister, her Aunt Harriet, was summoned, did she understand the truth. In August of 1854, when Libbie was twelve years old, lovely, gentle Sophia Bacon died, holding in her hand the portrait of her little daughter.

Her Aunt Harriet took the grief-dazed girl back to Grand

Rapids to stay with her mother's family while her father made plans for their sadly changed future. When she returned, Libbie reentered the Seminary as a boarding student, for her father had decided to rent his house and to live in a hotel. The Seminary occupied a large three-story building crowned by a cupola, with brick chimneys and two lower ells, all painted white with green blinds. It was set back from the street surrounded by trees and flowering shrubs and guarded by a wrought-iron fence.

The Reverend Boyd, principal of the school, had many ideas on female education which were criticized as far too "advanced." The higher education of women was still a much argued subject in 1854, but Judge Bacon had been a founder of the Seminary and was one of his staunchest supporters. He approved of the course of study, which included, in the primary department, not only reading, spelling, and arithmetic, but grammar and moral lessons as well. The academic department added higher geography, American history and French grammar to the basic subjects in its first year and in its second, anatomy, the history of Rome, philosophy, government and the analysis of "Thompson's Seasons."

As for the collegiate department, elementary algebra and higher arithmetic and the history of England appeared on the prospectus for the first year along with such usual subjects for young ladies as French, drawing and music. In the second year came chemistry and botany, with geometry and the history of France. Next, German, higher rhetoric, geometry and an analysis of Young's Night Thoughts were added.

In the crowning senior year the young ladies studied moral philosophy, geology, logic, astronomy, a criticism of Milton, mental philosophy and analogy. In addition to these formidable subjects to enrich the youthful mind, the Reverend Boyd had on his campus a well equipped gymnasium where his students were expected to maintain the health and vigor of their bodies as well—an almost unheard of requirement for "young ladies of delicacy and refinement" in those days.

As the daughter of one of the founders and also of a leading citizen of the town, Libbie lived as a "star boarder" at the Seminary. She had a bedroom and parlor to herself with a view out over the level streets of the town to the river and the more distant Lake Erie. The Judge visited her frequently. His dignified figure became a familiar sight to teachers and pupils, for all his affection was now centered on his only child. She spent her short holidays with him at his hotel and they always went to church together.

"Poor, motherless little girl!" the tender-hearted ladies of the congregation whispered together as they entered. Overhearing this for the first time brought Libbie to the brink of tears and the Judge was barely able to control his emotions. Later, as her grief grew less sharp, she learned that there were some advantages to her situation. Her father found it hard to refuse her anything, her classmates showered her with sympathy and affection, and even the teachers were indulgent to her faults. They excused absences from class, tardiness, and even unprepared lessons on the ground that "poor Libbie has no mother." "How shamefully I traded on this!" Libbie confessed long afterwards.

Judge Bacon kept his sisters informed of his daughter's progress. "Libbie seems to have regained her spirits. I find her without gloom, even happy at times," he wrote with relief.

All Libbie's vacations were now spent with her aunts, especially with her father's sisters at the Sabin Farm at Howlett's Hill, New York. Life there was carefree and gay, with parties, picnics, singing schools, and even dances, which the Judge never allowed in his own home. The years sped by. Libbie was growing up into an extremely pretty girl. Her small figure was slim and erect, her features delicate and regular, her hair a rich, glossy brown, her eyes gray-blue framed in long, dark lashes. Her greatest beauty, however, was a clear, transparent, dazzlingly white skin and cheeks always bright with color.

"You've got the prettiest girl in Monroe, Daniel," one of her father's friends, Judge Blanchard of nearby Tecumseh, told him. "You'll not have her on your hands for long. I'll warrant she has plenty of beaux already."

"Beaux!" the Judge echoed blankly. Sixteen-year-old Libbie was still a child to him, and the thought of beaux or of marriage filled him with alarm. He felt suddenly lonely and helpless. How could a father, a mere man, cope with the problems of the years ahead? He had bravely promised Sophia that he would take full care of their daughter, and he prided himself that he had managed to arrange Libbie's education very creditably. Here was a whole new set of difficulties looming ahead of him!

What was more, Libbie herself soon began to add to his worries. "I want a home of my own like other girls, somewhere to entertain my friends. Why can't we get our old house back from the renters and live there again, Pa?" she asked.

The Judge's problem was finally solved in an eminently logical way. Through that same Judge Blanchard he was introduced to a Mrs. Rhoda Pitts, the charming widow of a respectable clergyman. She was attractive, healthy, good-tempered, a notable housekeeper, and she seemed genuinely interested in becoming a second mother to Libbie. Libbie liked her, too, and in the spring of 1859 the Judge remarried.

While the house was being remodeled to suit their new needs, Libbie stayed at Howlett's Hill with her rollicking cousins. "Have all the fun you can, now, Libbie," they warned her. "You'll be made to toe the mark by your new stepmother. Wait and see!"

CHAPTER

2

Libbie returned to Monroe to find that her cousin's warning was quite groundless. The new Mrs. Bacon was energetic, neat as a pin, and presided faultlessly over the Judge's home, but she was also full of fun and laughter. From her kitchen emerged the best food Libbie had ever tasted.

"No more boarding at the Seminary with its weeks of mutton!" Libbie wrote in triumph to her cousin, Rebecca Richmond. " 'Mutton young, mutton old, mutton hot, mutton cold, mutton tender, mutton tough, thank the Lord we've had enough!' How tired we used to get of it!"

What was more surprising, Mrs. Bacon would not lay the slightest household task on the girl. "Now is the time for your schooling," she stated. "You are a bright girl, Libbie. You really should take highest honors when you graduate at the Seminary."

Spurred on by her confidence, Libbie went back to school determined to study harder than ever. There was plenty of time left for gaiety, too, and the Bacon home soon became the center for gatherings of pretty girls in full, swaying hoop-skirts and their attendant young gentlemen. The Judge still forbade dancing, but Libbie persuaded him to build one of the newly fashionable "piazzas" on the house and it was the scene of games and "promenades by couples to music," which were almost as much fun.

It was true that as the 1860's began, the talk, especially among the young men, was more and more about the probability of war between the states of the North and the South. Militia companies had been formed throughout Michigan and the boys of Monroe spent long hours drilling in trim, bright-colored uniforms. One of the most popular of the local beaux did not join, however. His home was in the South and, after protracted and romantic goodbyes to all the girls, he disappeared. "He's gone to join the forces of his native state!" it was whispered. His departure cast a sudden cold, foreboding shadow over the lighthearted group.

Judge Bacon deplored the "formidable rebellion" and shook his head gloomily as he read the papers aloud. Libbie and her mother listened dutifully, but politics was a subject reserved for gentlemen. Ladies, especially young girls, were not supposed to have opinions about such matters. At the risk of seeming daring and "advanced," Libbie declared her loyalty to the Union and her horror of slavery.

Even after so many months of alarmed discussion in the news, the actual firing on Fort Sumter and President Lincoln's call for troops came as a surprise and shock. For Libbie, war was something far away, unreal and almost impossible to imagine. Some men from Monroe enlisted and went away, but the boys she knew merely drilled harder than ever while the girls admired their brass buttons and gilt braid and increased the number of parties to honor the new-fledged heroes.

"If you really want to be of service to your country, Libbie," Mrs. Bacon suggested, when summer vacation began, "why don't you get some of your friends together and sew clothing for the families of our soldiers. That would be useful and pleasant, too. One of you could read aloud from some improving book while the rest of you worked."

A group was accordingly gathered in the Bacon parlor one warm afternoon. Smooth-brushed or carefully curled heads bent over their sewing while plump, conscientious Nettie Humphrey read aloud from a book on moral philosophy recommended by the Reverend Boyd. At the end of a chapter she laid it down with a sigh. "Philosophy is such a difficult subject," she said, "especially with no professor to explain it to us."

"It's begun to rain," Rita Jackson said, looking out of the window. "The boys will have to stop drilling or they'll spoil their uniforms."

"They won't stop just because of the rain, silly!" Nettie laughed. "That's no way to train to be soldiers, and ours are really working at it. My pa says that Monroe has the best-drilled militia company in the county. We have the most men already at the front, too. Two lieutenant colonels, three captains, and lots of other officers as well as privates. Autie Custer, Mrs. Reed's half-brother, was actually in that terrible fighting at Bull Run and he was mentioned in dispatches for bravery."

"Autie Custer?" Laura echoed. "Oh yes, he went to West Point, didn't he?"

Rita Jackson nodded her blonde curls. "Yes, although he graduated last in his class, I heard, with so many demerits that if the War hadn't broken out just then he wouldn't have received a commission at all! He's a lieutenant now, though, sure enough, and he really cuts a dash in his cavalry uniform. When he was here on leave the girls were forever finding excuses to call at Mrs. Reed's house. They spoke to him on the street and some even tapped out messages to him with their parasols on the fence in front of the house," she added, with a giggle.

Libbie drew her brows together, remembering. A picture had flashed into her mind with the name, the picture of a tall, blue-eyed boy whose hair had caught the sunlight long ago. The first day I had my swing, she recalled. Then the other time, when Laura dared me! Color suddenly warmed her cheeks. I was only a child, she told herself defensively. Those girls who are pursuing him now are old enough to know better. How bold and shameless they must be! She lifted her chin and drew her thread through the cloth with a sharp jerk.

Kind Annette looked distressed. "Yes, the girls do like Autie and they do run after him, but then, he *is* lots of fun. He's really a nice fellow, too."

Rita giggled again. "Have you ever seen his father, old Emmanuel Custer? He was here visiting last month. There never was such a talker—always spouting Democratic politics to anyone who'd listen. He even kept up a running argument with the conductor on the through train. They shouted at each other every time it went by."

"I've met the whole family," another girl put in. "They all talk fast and joke a lot, but they're really nice, respectable people, even though they *are* Democrats. Mrs. Reed's children are darlings."

"I've never seen them when they didn't have jam on their faces," Rita said. "Oh, well, West Point is supposed to be able to make gentlemen out of boys from any station in life. Maybe it's even made one out of Autie Custer!"

"What's the matter, Rita? Didn't he come out when *you* rapped on his fence with *your* parasol?" Laura asked with a teasing smile.

Rita flushed scarlet and was about to answer angrily when Mrs. Bacon entered with a tray of cocoa and cake. "It's time to light the lamps, Libbie," she said. "Girls mustn't strain their pretty eyes."

Libbie sprang up to fetch the lights and the slightly ruffled tempers were quickly smoothed over. Enough had been said, however, to establish Libbie's distaste for young Lieutenant Custer. Imagine having a father whom people laughed about! she thought. How thankful I should be that Pa's so dignified and admired.

Next to the War, the most important thing to Libbie Bacon in the spring of the following year of 1862 was her graduation from Boyd's Seminary. She had been chosen to deliver the valedictory address, proof that her year's efforts to study had been successful. "Although I still wonder how I ever stood up under such brain-work!" she wrote to one of her aunts.

Two cousins, Rebecca and Mary Richmond and an uncle, Abel Page, were invited to Monroe for the great occasion. Of course there had to be extra parties to honor the two girls. In spite of the Judge's rules against dancing, boat rides, and driving behind fast horses with fast young men, both cousins wrote home glowing accounts of their good times.

Before the graduation came an evening of piano recitals by the music students at which Libbie played a spirited polonaise. "The audience will kindly remain quiet during the musical numbers," a note on the program requested "because these compositions are difficult to play and require great concentration. Of course there will be no applause at the end, since these are Young Ladies, not Public Performers."

Annual addresses before the Young Ladies' Literary Society came on the Tuesday evening before Commencement. Then, at last, the great day arrived. There were ten other graduates besides Libbie. All were dressed alike in frocks of white Swiss muslin, modestly high-necked and long sleeved, slim in waist and bodice but billowing out like clouds over their hoops.

"Aren't you frightened, Libbie?" Laura whispered as they gathered in a fluttering group, ready to go into the hall where the audience waited.

Libbie pressed her palms to her crimson cheeks. "Of course I am!" she answered. "Look—we can see through this crack in the door. There's my father on the platform and everyone else in Monroe is there too, I think! Did you ever see so many ministers in black coats and white neck-cloths collected in one place?"

"We'll have to curtsey—how many times is it, Libbie?" Laura quavered.

"Three—or is it four?" Libbie said. "Oh Lord, I really can't remember. Once to the teachers, once to the trustees, once to the ministers and once to the audience. That makes four. Laura, I'm positive that my knees will give way under me. They're trembling already."

But when the signal came and the music struck up a lively march, Libbie and Laura and the other young graduates managed to gather themselves together and, thanks to years of training in deportment, entered the hall with an appearance of perfect composure.

The ceremonies lasted for over five hours. Finally came the time for the valedictory address, and Libbie mounted the platform. To Judge Bacon she looked beautiful as an angel in her frothy white muslin, and her likeness to her dead mother struck him so vividly that he could barely control his emotion. She made all her curtseys with pretty deference to the teachers, the trustees, the delegation of black-garbed ministers and, last of

genially. "She'd have taken up
you other girls."

thing to say!" Libbie protested.
e's a good advertisement for the
e Humphrey House. We fellows
the other day that he'd have to
n if he expected to carry her as a

nething better to do than to hang
bbie flung back.

_ibbie, don't be angry," kind,
d. "We're going to the loveliest
oil it before we get there."

y," Conway conceded, with a
veryone does, even if she _is_ fat."
t she pressed her lips together
might have replied. Laura was
l her the wrong way, but she
her pleasure this evening.

he girls gathered their volumi-
heir hoops out of the carriage.
ly crowded, as full of color and
. Most of the girls wore the
so fashionable that year. Libbie
r Mrs. Bacon's preference for
ill wear well and stand turning
somber color of her dress. But
the deep, rich hue set off the
s and shoulders and the close-
spreading skirt emphasized her

!" Laura told her warmly.

all, to the audience. She read her carefully phrased address in
a clear young voice and the paper shook only slightly in her
hands. Not Judge Bacon alone but the entire audience was
visibly touched when she curtseyed one last time down to the
floor with flawless grace, turned, and glided back to her seat.

Laura Noble pressed her hand. "You were wonderful, Libbie!" she whispered.

Libbie looked at her, pale and wide-eyed. "Is it over?" she
asked. "Laura, I can't remember a word I said. I think I was
terrified into a trance."

All the newspapers in the county wrote full accounts of the
occasion and Libbie clipped out the best of them and sent
copies to those of her relatives who had not been able to attend. "The Trustee who gave me my diploma pronounced me
a thoroughly educated young lady," she wrote. "He said I was
ready to take my place in the world. I wonder what it will be?"

Of course for any girl of her class and time the next goal
would logically be marriage. Already she had many attractive
beaux and some serious suitors. Soon, she knew, she would have
to choose among them and settle down to the well-ordered life
of a young matron, but Libbie was in no hurry. Being the belle
of Monroe was too much fun for her to wish to change her
status.

Among her admirers were numbers of young soldiers and
officers, dashing in their uniforms and appealingly romantic
in the aura of danger which surrounded them. Over and over
again, however, the Judge warned Libbie against taking any of
them seriously. "A girl must think of her future," he told her,
with deep concern. "Brass buttons and gilt braid are handsome,
it's true, but how often they are accompanied by drinking,
gambling, and other dissipations!" He shook his head solemnly.
"You will have to take my word for this, my dear, for such

sordid details are not for a young girl's ears. Why, only the
other day didn't I point out to you from this very window a
group of young officers so overcome with liquor that they
were positively staggering as they passed our house?"

"Yes, father," Libbie acknowledged, remembering the wild,
raucous laughter that had reached them from across the street.

"Never forget, either," the Judge continued, ominously,
"the agile uniformed youngster of today may be the hobbling,
dependent cripple of tomorrow."

Not that the Judge considered himself unpatriotic. He was
generous in his subscriptions to war charities and made many
speeches in support of the Union and the boys in blue. "If I
were younger, I would enlist myself," he often declared.

His only daughter was a different matter, however, and especially so as the War began to impress itself more and more
deeply upon the life of the town. Hollow-eyed young fellows
home with wounds or lingering fevers were to be seen everywhere, and the number of families mourning their dead increased relentlessly. Judge Bacon was determined to shelter his
lovely Elizabeth from any entanglement likely to bring her
anxiety and grief.

She had been brought up to be a dutiful and obedient daughter whenever her father gave definite commands, but he knew,
nevertheless, that she was young, tender-hearted and romantic.
"Our house is almost like a tavern with so much company
coming and going," the Judge wrote to a sister. "Many are of
the mustached, gilt-striped-and-buttoned kind. I greatly fear
that one of them will get our Libbie yet."

Throughout the summer the War ground on its inexorable
way. The papers were full for a time of the name of General
McClellan, whom the hopeful Lincoln had entrusted with the
command of the Army of the Potomac. Other names, those of

out Annette," Conway sai
as much space as all three o

"Conway! That's a mea

"Well, it's true, isn't it?
food at her father's hotel, t
were telling Jacob Greene
practice up at the gymnasi
bride across any threshold."

"You boys should have s
around hotels, gossiping!"

"Conway, stop teasing.
gentle Laura Noble entrea
party of the season. Don't

"Oh, very well, I'm s
grin. "I like Annette a lot.

Libbie tossed her head
and kept back whatever s
right. Conway often rub
wasn't going to let him sp

Arrived at the Seminar
nous skirts and maneuvere
The dressing room was al
perfume as a flower gar
pastel-hued, flounced tarla
had a moment of regret
"good, substantial silk tha
another season" and for t
the mirror showed her t
smooth whiteness of her
fitted bodice above the w
slender, supple waist.

"You look beautiful, Li

"Oh, I was just thinking how sweet that color of blue is on you," Libbie answered. "It's exactly the shade of your eyes."

The three friends gave each other's hands a brief pressure as they turned toward the door. Parties were so thrilling! A girl never knew whom she might meet. Beyond that door, excitement, romance, even fate itself might be waiting!

The three curtseyed to their hostess and the other ladies in the receiving line and at once were swept into the gay, noisy throng. Libbie found herself disappointingly beside Conway and was about to turn away when he touched her arm. "Wait a moment, Libbie," he pleaded. "Let's be friends again. There's someone who wants to meet you—a real celebrity. It's Autie Custer, Captain Custer now, back on leave. He's an aide-de-camp on the staff of General McClellan, no less, and he has all sorts of citations to his credit. I've promised to introduce him to the prettiest girl in the room and, of course, that's *you*."

Autie Custer! Libbie caught her breath. Excitement, curiosity and also a quick, unreasoning sense of panic swept through her. Conway was waiting, however, and she nodded with outward composure. "Very well," she answered and unfurled her fan with fingers that seemed to have gone suddenly cold.

He disappeared in the throng and almost instantly was back again, murmuring their names in introduction. Libbie was conscious of a blue uniform and of brass buttons and gold braid shining in the glow of the gas-lit crystal chandelier just above them. It's ridiculous to feel so nervous, she thought. He couldn't possibly remember that moment's incident so long ago, and what if he did? Yet why else did his eyes hold hers with such fixed smiling attention. It was as though he were about to laugh at something—at her! She lowered her lashes and fluttered her fan to cool her glowing cheeks.

"Captain Custer," she acknowledged. "I understand that your promotion has been very rapid. What an honor to be on the staff of General McClellan!"

His hair was as curly and as yellow as ever and he still wore it slightly long, his face as sunburnt, his eyes as blue. He had changed very little from the schoolboy she remembered, for all his lean, erect height and the sweep of the cavalry mustache that hid his mouth.

"I have been very fortunate," he answered. "It is warm in here. May I have the privilege?" He took her fan from her and she saw, as he fanned her, that his hands were unusually large, square, and muscular. "Will you forgive me if I confess that our friend Conway mumbled your name so that it was difficult for me to catch? And I'm sure it's a lovely name, if it matches its owner."

Her panic vanished. He didn't remember. She looked up, her eyes brimming with mischief. "My name? Oh, Miss Smith," she answered. "Not too difficult a name to catch, was it, Captain Custer?"

He threw back his head and laughed as though what she had said delighted him utterly. His laugh was loud, abrupt and startling. His voice, too, was loud and a little harsh and he spoke so fast that she could not always follow the flow of his words as he answered the usual questions young ladies were supposed to ask about his part in the War.

After what had seemed only a few moments of conversation, Libbie became conscious of a different sound—the tuning of violins—and glanced about in surprise. The crowd had moved away from them leaving them alone in the center of the floor under the sparkling crystal. "Oh!" she exclaimed in dismay. "The musical program must be starting. It's to be in the next room."

"Then let me escort you there, Miss Smith," he said, and offered his arm.

Libbie laid her fingers on the blue and gold of Captain Custer's sleeve and glided beside him as they followed the others through the arched doorway.

CHAPTER

3

When Libbie and Anna returned from the party, they found Nettie huddled sleepily before the dining room fire, waiting for them. "Tell me *all* about it," she begged as the three tiptoed up the stairs to Libbie's room.

"Unhook me first, there's a dear," Anna said, and sighed with relief as her waist was freed from its tight stays. "Oh, it was wonderful! And you should have seen Libbie. She captured the lion of the evening. He never left her side from the moment they were introduced."

"Everyone missed you, Nettie," Libbie told her. "So many spoke of wishing you had been there."

"Even Captain Custer?" Anna asked, mischievously.

"Autie Custer?" Nettie exclaimed. "Was he there? Now you've met him at last, Libbie, what do you think of him? Don't you think him handsome? And so dashing!"

"It was plain enough what he thought of *her*," Anna said, with a giggle. "Even when he thought she was 'Miss Smith.' "

"Miss Smith?" Nettie echoed. "Oh, you girls are so provoking. You must tell me everything. You promised!"

Libbie hesitated. Her eyes held an odd, dreamy look, different from their usual sparkle as she began to undress slowly.
"There isn't much to tell. Conway introduced him and he
didn't catch my name so I told him that I was 'Miss Smith,'
just for fun. He soon found out the truth, though, and we
had a good laugh over it."

"Didn't you like him, Libbie? He is a real celebrity, you
know. Jacob Greene says that General McClellan singled him
out for special praise many times. What did you talk about?"

"I really don't remember," Libbie answered vaguely. "The
usual things about the War, I suppose. That's all that men
are interested in, now. At any rate *he* did most of the
talking."

Nettie was persistent. "You haven't answered my question. Didn't you like him, Libbie?"

Standing barefooted in her long, full nightdress Libbie
began to brush her hair with slow strokes. "Well, he was
very pleasant and very flattering," she conceded. "Almost
too much so," she added quickly. "It really gave me a turn
to have him ask to call on so short an acquaintance."

"What did you answer? I suppose your father would hardly
allow that. Did you refuse?" Nettie asked.

Libbie shook her head. "No, I didn't refuse, exactly," she
admitted. "That would have been very unkind to one of our
brave soldiers, but I did manage not to be definite. He'll be
at singing school at Mrs. Paulding's on Monday. I agreed
to see him there."

Libbie was the first to awake the next morning. She lay
for a little while in the great bed listening to her friends'
placid breathing and thinking over the evening before. Captain Custer's high-colored, hawk-nosed face was startlingly
clear in her mind. She gave her head a little shake as though

to disturb the image, slipped out of bed and dressed herself, then went quietly down the stairs.

In the dining room her stepmother greeted her. "Ah, good morning my dear. Augusta's busy, so I'll bring you some breakfast. Did you have a nice time at the Boyd's party?"

"Oh yes, a lovely time," Libbie answered, but with no special enthusiasm in her voice.

"Your father has already gone downtown to his office. He told me not to disturb you girls. 'They need their beauty sleep,' he said," Mrs. Bacon continued, returning from the kitchen with an appetizing tray-full.

To her surprise Libbie caught her around the waist and gave her a vehement hug. "You are both so good to me!" she cried. "Everyone says that you spoil me, and how I love it!"

"Careful—you'll upset the cream!" Mrs. Bacon laughed. "You must have had a wonderful time, Libbie. Did you meet a new beau? I seem to recognize the signs."

"Oh no, nobody special," Libbie found herself answering quickly and set to work on her breakfast with a great show of appetite.

"This cold weather has got me to wondering about your winter coat," Mrs. Bacon said, settling her rustling starched calico into a chair. "I think your last year's will do nicely for every day. I had it out this morning to look it over and all it needs is fresh braid around the hem. Suppose you take it over to Miss Milligan right away, as soon as you're finished, before the other girls come down. She's quick and clever and if you get it to her early she'll have it ready for you tomorrow. Be sure to wear your red hood and your warm shawl—the wind is like ice."

Libbie set out soon after with the coat over her arm. Al-

though the sky was blue the ground was crisp with frost
and wind rocked the leafless boughs overhead. It tugged at
her hood so that she paused once to retie the strings under
her chin and to draw the shawl closer about her shoulders.

Miss Milligan's shop was in the next block on Monroe
Street, in one of the first of the brick buildings that marked
the town's business section. As she neared it Libbie saw a
tall, blue-clad figure coming toward her, walking with a rapid,
swinging stride that looked familiar. It was Captain Custer.

She felt her heart give a thump, then it began to race and
her breath caught. I don't want to meet him here in the
public street, not in this childish hood and carrying an old
coat! she thought. Has he recognized me? She turned hastily
into Miss Milligan's doorway and rang the bell.

The dressmaker was slow in answering, and while Libbie
waited she stole a quick look over her shoulder. The young
officer caught her glance and took off his hat with a flourish.
He seemed about to stop and speak to her, but at that moment
the door opened. With a hasty, acknowledging nod, Libbie
fled inside.

Miss Milligan greeted her with pleasure. "Come in out of
the wind, Miss Libbie. Sure and what a fine color it's given
you, my dear. Ah, the coat I made for you last year? Let me
have a look at it."

The coat was ready to wear over Libbie's new blue merino
dress to singing school the following Monday. Instead of a
bonnet or hood, she wore one of the fashionable "fascinators,"
a scarf crocheted of lacy wool to match her dress and worn
like a Spanish mantilla. Anna had gone to stay for a few
days with another school friend before her return to Toledo,
so the Judge walked with Libbie over to Mrs. Paulding's
door, then returned to his own fireside.

Mrs. Paulding's singing school provided the young people of Monroe with one of their favorite diversions. Her house was large, her piano a fine instrument, and she herself was an enthusiastic musician. Under her direction they practiced "part singing" of the latest ballads, sentimental or humorous, as well as hymns and classical oratorios. The girls were brought to the house by father or brother, but going home they were escorted by whatever young gentleman had won the privilege, which added the zest of competition to the evening. Most of the young men confessed boldly that they really had little interest in music but that they came for the chance of seeing some special girl to her home.

"Good evening, Miss Bacon—or is it Miss Smith again?" Captain Custer held out his hand and Libbie put hers into it. It was swallowed up in his big grasp and he did not let it go. "Don't forget that I'm to have the honor of escorting you home."

"But I don't remember—" Libbie said in surprise. "Did I promise you that, really?"

"Didn't you? Perhaps I misunderstood, but I've been counting on it ever since," he said. "Please say that I may?"

He was still holding her hand and she noticed that they had begun to attract attention. "Why yes, if you'd like to, Captain Custer," she answered. "But please give me back my hand."

He looked down at it with a great show of surprise. "Forgive me! I didn't realize that I still had it. It's so tiny and so soft! Then that's settled. You've made me the happiest man here, Miss Bacon."

They took their places on the rows of chairs set out near the piano, gentlemen on one side, ladies on the other. Mrs. Paulding rapped for silence, the hum of conversation stopped and the class began. Custer's singing, like his speaking voice, was loud, but it was clear and true and he plainly enjoyed it. In some of the sentimental ballads he sang with evident emotion. Watching him, Libbie was surprised to see that during one affecting passage about the death of a little child his eyes actually glistened with tears!

A soldier, fresh from battlefields, and still so sensitive? she thought with wonder. His hand had been hard and calloused from holding a cavalry sabre—she could still feel its roughness—yet there he was singing a foolish, sentimental song with tears in his blue eyes. A quick warmth swept through her and she felt her own eyes brimming.

From Mrs. Paulding's home to the Bacon house was only a few blocks, but for once Captain Custer was not in a hurry. At the bridge over the river they paused to look down at the water rippling with silver moonlight. "The Raisin River," Libbie said. "How pretty and peaceful it looks now! And to think that some of our own townspeople can remember the awful Indian massacre that happened right here, almost where we are standing. Stories about it have given me my very worst nightmares."

"Do you believe in ghosts, Miss Bacon?" Custer asked. His voice sank to a whisper. "There might be some around us now. *Look there, right behind you!*"

Libbie whirled with a little shriek and felt his arms close around her. "Don't worry, I'll protect you," he said, and she could feel that he was laughing.

She freed herself indignantly. "You are very presumptuous, Captain Custer," she said. With her head held stiffly high she began to walk as fast as she could.

"I'm sorry. It was only a joke. *Please* forgive me," he begged, hurrying beside her.

His face in the moonlight was so penitent and woebegone that she relented. "Oh, very well," she said, grudgingly. Then his expression of relieved delight was so comical that she could not help laughing. They were chatting light-heartedly again when they reached her home. "I'd like to call on you tomorrow," he said, swinging the gate open for her.

"If you wish. At three o'clock," she told him. "Goodnight, Captain Custer."

"Goodnight, Miss Bacon." He swept off his hat, bowed over her gloved hand. "Until tomorrow!" He was still stand-ing there gazing after her as she entered the lighted doorway.

Her father looked up from his chair beside the lamp on the parlor table when she entered. "Ah, Libbie," he said. "Was that Conway Noble who brought you home?"

"Oh no, Father, it was Captain Custer," she answered.

He frowned. "Custer? Mrs. Reed's half-brother?"

"Yes, Father," Libbie replied. "He—" She had started to mention that he would be calling the next day, but suddenly thought better of it.

"Well, it's late, Libbie. Run up to bed," he said, and placed a marker in his book. "I'll put out the lights."

At breakfast the next day Libbie learned that her father had an errand which would take him some miles up the river to look at some property, and that he would be away from home for the rest of the week. Only after he had gone, driving his fast-stepping trotter in the "shay," did she mention to her stepmother, as casually as she could, that Captain Custer would call that afternoon.

Mrs. Bacon looked disturbed. "You should have asked your father, Libbie," she said. "I don't know what he'll say when he hears about this."

"It really quite slipped my mind," Libbie answered airily, then felt herself blushing. Embarrassed by her fib and furious at herself now for telling it, she blushed even more under her stepmother's probing look.

"Ah, so that's how it is!" Mrs. Bacon began to smile. "Well, it can't be helped now, I suppose. Let's see—I think I'll just whip up some of my little sponge cakes to serve with the tea."

The tall clock in the Bacon parlor was just striking three when Captain Custer came whistling through the gate and mounted the porch steps with a bound. "Heavens! How prompt he is!" Libbie said, and fled up the stairs to her room. While she waited to be summoned she held her hands high in the air—the usual practice of young ladies before receiving callers—so that her hands would look white and fragile. There was no need to pinch her cheeks to make them red. Her mirror told her that her color was already high.

Soon Augusta, the stout "hired girl" came toiling up the stairs. "He's here, Mis' Libbie," she announced. "Mis' Bacon says for you to come on down."

Libbie waited, however, until the woman had descended and gone back into the kitchen before she herself emerged, came down the stairs and entered the parlor with the smooth, floating glide that hoop-skirts made so effective.

The call was conducted on the formal lines laid down by etiquette. Captain Custer commented on the weather, the handsome furnishings of the parlor, the engraved equestrian portrait of General Winfield Scott on one wall and of General Sam Houston on another, and especially on the oil painting of Libbie herself at ten. He praised the tea and complimented the little frosted cakes by eating several.

"Let us hear some of your experiences in the War," Mrs. Bacon requested. "Nothing too terrible, of course. Is it true that there were some royal princes on General McClellan's staff?"

"Yes, that's a fact, ma'am," he answered. "The Count of Paris and the Duke of Chartres, grandsons of King Louis Phillippe. The Duke is the so-called pretender to the French throne, so the Emperor Napoleon III has exiled them from their country. Nice, friendly fellows, not in the least haughty. Their uncle, the old Prince de Joinville, keeps his eye on them as well as he can, but they manage to have a good time in spite of him and even got into some hot fighting at Gainses' Mill."

"Tell me," Libbie asked. "Aren't you *ever* afraid in danger?"

He grinned. "Well, we learn not to show it. Most of the time we're too busy to have time to be afraid, but I'll tell you once I was as scared as I ever want to be. It was last May, on the Peninsula. General McClellan had one of those new-fangled gas balloons sent up to overlook the enemy positions and spy on them. The balloonists themselves weren't qualified to bring down adequate military reports, so he sent up General Porter. While he was up there the wind changed and it looked for a while as though he would be blown over enemy territory and captured, so General McClellan gave orders that a less valuable observer would have to make the ascent. I was a second lieutenant, then, the cheapest they could find, I guess, so the job fell to me."

"You actually went up into the sky in a balloon?" Libbie breathed.

"It seems almost sacrilegious!" Mrs. Bacon faltered.

"I'll never forget it," he said. "I wasn't a bit eager to go, but orders are orders, so I climbed in, the mooring ropes were let loose, and up we went. The basket looked mighty flimsy to carry two men so high above the earth, and I said so to the balloonist. Then what did the fellow do but jump up and down on the frame to show me how strong it was! I guess I turned green, for he laughed at me all the rest of the day about it. After the first, though, it wasn't bad and I got so I really enjoyed the flights."

He stayed only a little longer than the approved hour and a half, then bowed gallantly to both ladies and departed. "A pleasant, well-mannered young man," Mrs. Bacon commented after he had gone. "Really, I don't see how Daniel could find any fault with him. If only he were not an officer! He did seem to enjoy my sponge cakes, didn't he? I'm so glad I took the time to make them."

"Then it was all right that I accepted his invitation to the oyster supper over at the Inn on the lake?" Libbie asked.

"Well, I suppose so, since Mrs. Paulding is to chaperone you," her stepmother said. "But I still worry about what Daniel will say."

Later that week Libbie sat at her desk, busy with letters. "I have the escort of one of General McClellan's staff whenever I put my nose out of doors," she wrote to her cousin, Rebecca Richmond. And to Laura Noble, visiting in New York, she wrote, "He is constantly in attendance. My friends tease me about him, but I don't *really* care for him except as an escort."

For a time she sat looking at the words she had written and nibbling thoughtfully at the end of her pen. Once she dipped the point into the ink and started to cross out the last clause, then changed her mind. She enjoyed being with him. His jokes and high spirits kept her laughing, but sometimes she found herself irritated by his loud and rapid voice and his taut, high-keyed, restless energy. I do find him rather fascinating, but I don't really care for him, she decided. She finished and sealed her letter.

Judge Bacon returned on Saturday. "I'll have to tell him about Captain Custer's attentions to you, of course, Libbie," her stepmother warned her. "Oh, dear, I really wonder how he'll take it."

Libbie was summoned into the parlor where her father sat waiting. "Sit down, my dear," he told her, his face grave. "I need not tell you how disturbed I am by the information your mother has given me. You know that you should have waited for my permission before inviting a young man to my house."

"You were away, Father," Libbie stammered. She was looking down at her hands clasped tightly in her lap.

"For a few days only," he corrected her. He paused, then began again. "I will admit that Captain Custer has a fine military record. I have heard it well spoken of by men whose opinions I value. But as an escort for my daughter—" he shook his head.

"Mother thought well of him too," Libbie ventured.

"Your mother is admirable, but she is like most women when it comes to judging character. She is easily swayed by a good appearance and by flattery." He paused again, then cleared his throat. "There are two reasons why I wish you to discontinue your association with this young man. The first reason is, perhaps, arbitrary. I have too much concern for your future to allow you to become in any way interested in an army officer. The risk to your welfare and happiness is too great. The other reason concerns the young man's personal character."

Libbie looked up in surprise. "His character? But what

fault can you find with his character when you don't know
him?"

"Do you remember some months ago when I called your
attention to two young officers, both deeply under the influence of drink, passing our house?" he asked. "One of them
was young Custer!"

Libbie gave a gasp of shocked dismay. "Are you sure?"
She remembered the distasteful scene only too well. "How
can you be so certain?"

"I know him by sight, even though I do not know him
personally," the Judge stated. "Yes, it was he. I saw them
turn in at Mr. Reed's house."

Tears were stinging Libbie's eyelids. She could find nothing
to say.

"I realize that such conduct is regrettably common, but
I could never excuse or condone it where it concerns you. I
have made up my mind on this point. Please do not receive
this young man again here in my house and please do not
accept his escort anywhere in the future. And do not com-
municate with him in any way, either."

"But—but—" Libbie faltered. "He is coming here this afternoon. He knows that you are expected today and he has
asked to be presented to you."

"I shall not be here when he arrives," her father said. "And
I expect you to explain my wishes to him courteously but
firmly. That will be all, my dear."

He rose, and Libbie got somehow to her feet, also. "But
father—" she protested. "How *can* I—?" Her throat tightened
and choked off the words.

"You have heard my wishes, Elizabeth," the Judge said.
"Now go up to your room. A quiet reading of a few Bible
passages will help you to compose your thoughts. Please

remember, my dear, that I am acting in the certainty that this is best for you."

Libbie swallowed hard, fighting to hold back her tears. In her room she closed her door, then stood leaning with her back against it. She had expected her father to be displeased and to lecture her severely, but never anything like this! How could he have put the burden of an explanation upon her? Never in all her life had she faced such an ordeal.

She heard the clock strike slowly below in the parlor. It was ten o'clock, and Captain Custer was coming at three.

CHAPTER

Prompt as always, Custer came whistling up the street. Libbie herself in a dove-gray dress with white collar and cuffs, opened the door for him. The quick, eager brightening of his face when he saw her gave her such a pang that she faltered in her stiff little greeting.

"Please come in, Captain Custer," she said. She preceded him into the parlor, her skirts rustling over the carpet. "Please sit down." She seated herself in a small chair and indicated another for him some distance away.

He looked surprised and started to move his chair nearer. "Oh no, please sit over there," she told him quickly.

"Wherever you say, Miss Libbie," he said. He looked puzzled for a moment, then his face seemed to clear. "Did your father return? Am I to have the honor of meeting him?"

She drew in her breath. "Father did return, but he is not at home at the present. Captain Custer—" Her voice died away and she sat looking at him helplessly.

"Is something wrong, Miss Libbie? You seem disturbed.

Have I done anything, said anything to displease you? Surely you know—"

She interrupted hurriedly. "It's my father," she said. "He—he disapproves of our acquaintance. He wishes me to discontinue it. He has forbidden me to ask you here again or to accept your escort any more or—or even to write to you!"

There, it was said, but not at all in the way she had planned. She had blurted it all out at once instead of leading up to it kindly and gently, as she had practiced during those hours since morning. Her lips felt stiff and cold as she sat staring at him, wide-eyed, while she twisted her lace handkerchief in both her hands.

Color rushed to the roots of his fair hair and his eyes had never looked so burningly blue. Suddenly he was on his feet and across the room at one stride, towering above her. "Libbie!" he said. "I love you devotedly. Will you marry me?"

She was never so astonished in her life. "But—but didn't you understand me? My father doesn't want us to meet any more. He'd never allow us to marry."

"But *you*, Libbie. Surely you know that he's being ridiculously unjust. If you love me—"

She rose from her chair to confront him, her cheeks flaming. "I have never indicated in any way that I loved you, Captain Custer!" she said. "But I *do* love and trust my father!"

"Then you, too, wish our friendship to end?" he asked. His high color was draining away and he looked pale as he gazed down upon her.

"I—" She faltered again, and she couldn't meet his eyes. "I am truly sorry," she said at last. "I—I have enjoyed our acquaintance. But unless he changes his mind I have no choice."

There was a long silence while the pendulum of the tall

clock filled the room with its measured, monotonous beat. At last Libbie looked up. He was standing stiffly erect and he was still very pale. "Very well," he answered. "I hope some day to change your father's opinion of me, but until that time I shall respect his wishes, since you feel that you must obey him. But may I ask one favor of you?"

"What is it?" Libbie asked tremulously.

"May I have a picture of you to take back with me to the battlefields? I would cherish it through all dangers. I had planned to ask you for it when I came, and I even brought one of mine to give to you in exchange. I hope you will accept it in spite of what has happened."

How could she refuse? "Why, yes," she said. A small ambrotype of her, recently taken, was in a drawer of her mother's desk. And she fetched it for him. He looked at it for a long moment, then placed it inside his officer's tunic and drew out one of himself.

"And something else," he said. "When I receive my orders to return to the fighting front, may I call here for one last time to say goodbye?"

Her voice was choked to a faint whisper, but she managed to answer. "Oh, yes, of course."

He gave a short, jerky bow, wheeled and left the room. She heard the front door open and shut, his step on the porch, and then he was gone. Libbie stood listening until the last footfall had died away, then fled up the stairs to her room, his picture in her hand. Once there she flung herself face down on her bed and wept, sobbing uncontrollably into the smooth linen of her pillow.

Annette Humphrey's round cheerful face was sober as she came to see her friend a few days later. "Libbie, whatever is the trouble between you and Autie Custer? I knew something was wrong when he took Fanny Fifield home from singing school instead of you. Then yesterday he came to see me and told me about what you had said to him. What is it that your father has against Autie? I know that your father is afraid to have you marry a soldier, but is there anything else?"

"I'm afraid there is, Nettie," Libbie told her. "You know how Father feels about drink. Well, he remembers seeing Captain Custer and another officer pass this very house, both so intoxicated that they could hardly walk. He pointed them out to me, although at the time I didn't know who they were. It was really a disgraceful sight!" And she shuddered at the memory.

To her surprise Nettie gave an exclamation of relief. "Was that all? Well, I can set both your minds to rest, then. Lydia Reed, his sister, told me about it when it happened. She is as strict as your father and she was so upset about it that then and there she made Autie promise on his word of honor that he would never drink another drop of intoxicating liquor, and he never has, since that day. Believe me, Libbie, I know him well and I know that he would die before he would break his word, once it was given."

"Oh, Nettie!" Libbie flung herself into her friend's arms. "I'm so *glad* you told me. I'll explain it to Father. I think it shows that Captain Custer has true firmness of character, don't you?" Then her face clouded again. "But that doesn't change the fact that he's an officer, and I'm afraid that's Father's chief objection. How can he hold to it, though, when every worthwhile young man is in the Army now? Does he want me to marry an old man or an invalid or a coward? It's either that or live single all the rest of my life—" Libbie's voice wavered off into silence at prospect of the bleak future threatening her.

"Surely he'll change his mind," Nettie suggested.

Libbie shook her head. "He's very stubborn, especially if anyone argues with him. If he changes his mind, it'll have to be of his own accord," she said. "He's so sure, always, that he's right! He suggested that I accept Anna Cotton's invitation to go home to Toledo with her for a visit. I think he expects it to be 'out of sight, out of mind' for me."

"Doesn't he know the other proverb—'absence makes the heart grow fonder'?" Nettie smiled.

Libbie looked troubled. "The difficulty is that I'm not really sure about my heart," she said. "Maybe a change of scene will help me to decide."

The Judge drove Anna Cotton and Libbie to the railroad station, then left them on the platform while he superintended the loading on and checking of their trunks. He returned to find the two girls being assisted up the high train steps by a young man in Army blue. Libbie was very conscious of the disapproval in her father's face at the liberty, and she saw how stiffly he avoided Custer's attempt at a friendly greeting.

Seated inside the car both girls waved and nodded out of the window and Libbie took a rebellious pleasure in giving as many of her smiles to the young officer as to the Judge. He really *is* stubborn and unreasonable, she thought. If I were a stranger before him in court he'd be scrupulously fair, but just because I'm his daughter he can see only his side of the case.

Libbie found Toledo a gay, busy place. Together with Anna she attended so many parties that she had to write home for another evening gown, which brought a reproving letter from her father. Was it wise for a young girl away from home to go out so often? There was no telling whom she might meet, and without a parent there to supervise, might she not make another mistake in giving her friendship to someone unworthy?

He took the opportunity to say how shocked he had been to see young Custer assisting her bodily up the steps of the car. Surely she knew better than to allow any young man such familiarity! He himself had heard a great deal of gossip since then connecting her name with that officer's and she could understand how it had distressed him.

Libbie's reply was respectful but spirited. She had gone to the Toledo parties, it was true, but she had also attended a wonderful concert by the famed musicians, Gottschalk and Patti. She had also attended a lecture on "Temperance" by one John B. Gough, and reported herself delighted by it.

As for the gossipers, she wished them all sunk in the sea! Surely he must remember that Captain Custer had assisted Anna Cotton up the steps as much as he had her. Even though she liked Captain Custer very well, she was obeying her father's wishes, and had not expected him to be at the station at all. She had not promised never to *see* him again, but she would cause her father no more anxiety, of that he could be sure. If only he would show some confidence in her!

News of the War continued to be somber. While Libbie was still in Toledo a great battle was fought at Fredericksburg in which General Burnside, who had succeeded General McClellan as commander of the Army of the Potomac, was badly defeated by General Lee. Libbie remembered how Custer had maintained that Burnside was an unworthy successor to his idolized chief. His opinion now seemed justified.

When she returned to Monroe, Nettie told her that Custer had been summoned to report to McClellan. "Has McClellan been put in command again?" Libbie asked. Her breath caught. "Will *he* be soon at the fighting front?"

Nettie shook her head. "Autie said that he was to help the General write his report of his campaigns," she answered. "He will be at Trenton."

Libbie let out the breath she had been holding. He had not had his chance to say goodbye. Would she ever see him again? The question swept over her in a wave that left her suddenly cold.

Christmas came and went and then New Year's Day with its strings of holiday callers at the Bacon home. Libbie wrote to her cousin that the visitors were pleasant, with "fewer dull ones than usual." She smiled brightly in answer to their greetings and compliments while Judge Bacon beamed with affectionate approval. The stormy interlude over "that mustached fellow" seemed to have slipped smoothly into the past, he decided.

A few weeks later Mrs. Bacon left town to visit relatives and the Judge decided that he and Libbie should take their meals at the Humphrey House while she was gone. Libbie was entering the lobby late one afternoon where she was to meet her father, her cheeks red with the cold above her fur muff, when Nettie beckoned to her mysteriously from the doorway of her sitting room. As soon as they were inside and the door shut behind them a uniformed figure stepped out of the shadows. It was Custer!

"I got a few days leave from General McClellan and of course I came here," he explained. "Libbie, I love you! No, never mind about Nettie. She knows all about it and she arranged this meeting for me. You promised to let me see you once more, remember, before I went to the front?"

"Are—are you going to the front *now?*" Libbie asked. Suddenly, with a little rush, she was in his arms. "Oh no! I can't bear to have you go into danger again!" she sobbed, lifting her tear-stained face to meet his kisses.

Neither of them noticed that Nettie had disappeared. After what seemed only the briefest of intervals she was back. "Libbie! Your father is out there looking for you. I heard him ask in the lobby if you had arrived. Thank goodness he didn't catch sight of me and ask me!"

"Come, Libbie, we'll have to face him and tell him how we feel," Custer said, looking down at her fondly. "When he knows you really care, I'm sure he'll relent."

But Libbie drew back in alarm. "Oh no, you don't know him," she said. "It would only make things worse if we confronted him suddenly, like this."

"You still feel you must obey him?" He was frowning. "But I'll be leaving. If he still forbids it, won't you even write to me or let me write to you?"

She hung her head miserably. "I can't. I promised."

He turned and began to stride up and down the room. Suddenly he wheeled about. "I have it! I'll write to Nettie, here, and she will show you my letters. Then you can tell her what to write to me. Nobody could object to my corresponding with my good friend Annette Humphrey—except Jake Greene, of course, and we'll explain to him."

So it was arranged. After a lingering goodbye Custer left by another door, Libbie straightened her bonnet, composed herself and glided demurely out into the lobby where the impatient Judge was looking at his big gold watch. "Ah, there you are, Elizabeth," he said, snapping the watch-case shut. "You are at least fifteen minutes behind the time we appointed to meet here. What kept you?"

"I went into Nettie's room and we were talking," she answered. "You know how girls are, Father. I'm very sorry."

The Judge peered at her sharply. She did not look at all sorry. There seemed to be traces of tears on her lashes but her eyes sparkled like stars and her cheeks glowed. She looks radiant, he thought, as radiant as a bride. *As a bride!* The phrase gave him a sharp jolt, and he glanced about the lobby. He had heard somewhere that that fellow Custer was in town.

A few weeks later Judge Bacon was passing through the hotel lobby again when he saw a group of his elderly friends gathered around an Army officer whose back was turned to him. The young man was answering their queries about the military situation clearly and interestingly, and the Judge joined the circle. When he discovered that the officer was Custer, it was too late to withdraw.

They were formally introduced, and the Judge was unable to suppress his interest in the replies Custer gave and even asked some questions of his own. In one of the pauses he cleared his throat. "I should much appreciate hearing from you directly from time to time and receive some first-hand information about how the War progresses," he said.

"Why, thank you, sir," the young Captain answered respectfully. "I'd be honored, and I shall take the first opportunity as soon as I return to my regiment." Blue eyes alight with pleasure, he was about to continue when the Judge, as though suddenly recollecting something, muttered an excuse, and hurried away.

Custer returned to General McClellan, who was now living in New York, and resumed his work on his commander's reports. In the middle of April he received orders to rejoin his company. It was a blow to part from the leader he admired. McClellan, too, regretted losing so devoted an admirer. Later, in his memoirs, he wrote his impression of his young aide. "A reckless, gallant boy, undeterred by fatigue, unconscious of danger. His head was always clear in danger and he always brought me clear and intelligible reports. I became much attached to him."

It was a further blow for Custer to lose his temporary rank of Captain, now that he was no longer on the staff of a commanding general. As Lieutenant Custer, once again, he arrived in Falmouth, Virginia, where the army was encamped. There he reported as an aide to General Pleasanton, now in command of a division of the reorganized Cavalry Corps. All these changes he wrote in long letters to Annette, which she relayed at once to Libbie. Judge Bacon also received a letter from the young man, still praising McClellan and expressing doubt over General Hooker, who had replaced the defeated Burnside in command of the Army of the Potomac.

Soon news reached Monroe of another great battle. Libbie's hands shook as she held the paper and pored over the gloomy accounts. Chancellorsville was a defeat for Hooker and might have been a fatal disaster for the Union cause if it had not been for the cavalry under General Pleasanton. Her heart pounding with mingled terror and pride, she read how Pleasanton's scouts had met Stonewall Jackson's flanking march and halted it just in time to prevent utter rout. For this coup Pleasanton was to be given command of the whole Cavalry Corps.

A letter to Annette soon told more about this change, from Custer's point of view. "He's to be a Major General, they say, so all of us on his staff will surely be promoted, too. I'm due to be a captain again," he exulted. He had an orderly now, a fine young soldier named Joseph Fought who was especially good with horses. He wrote, too, of acquiring a two-month-old puppy and gave enthusiastic accounts of the good meals he enjoyed as aide to the General. "Onions and radishes, tomatoes, asparagus, fresh fish, beef, mutton, veal, bacon, cake, oranges, ginger-snaps, candies, peas, hot biscuits, fresh milk, butter, cheese and everything." The General had a servant couple to cook for him. The dismal defeat was a thing of the past. The lieutenant's mind was cheerfully on the present and the future.

There was a silence of several weeks during which Libbie's anxiety took the form of wild nightmare dreams. Then came another long letter to Annette with a colorful account of a raid deep into enemy country on which Custer had been sent as aide representing the General. Seventy-five men and their horses had been shipped secretly by night on small steamers down the Potomac. Set ashore in one of the tidewater inlets, they had ridden forty miles inland into enemy country hoping to intercept a party of civilians reported to be carrying a large amount of money and important mail bound from Richmond to Urbana.

It was the sort of daring enterprise Custer loved best. They did not find the party they were looking for, but managed to capture a number of prisoners, thirty fine horses, some boxes of boots and shoes and, best of all, returned safely without losing a man. General Hooker himself complimented young Custer on his part in the success of the expedition.

In June Libbie read in the Michigan papers long stories boasting of the gallantry of a Michigan officer, Lieutenant George Armstrong Custer, at the battle of Aldie. In a cavalry skirmish between Pleasanton's men and those of the Confederate J. E. B. Stuart under Fitzhugh Lee and Wade Hampton, Custer's colonel had been shot down. Young Custer had thereupon assumed command and led a charge with such magnetic courage and confidence that the troopers rallied and followed him as though inspired. Surely, the papers continued, Governor Blair should heed the endorsements of six well-known generals and give this young veteran command of the newly recruited Michigan regiment. General Hooker had asserted that "we have no more gallant man in the field."

Judge Bacon read this last item aloud, then shook his head. "A strange idea, indeed! I'm surprised at an editor entertaining such a notion. Young Custer has a certain reckless bravery of course, everyone admits that. But Governor Blair is far too wise and prudent to appoint a lieutenant of twenty-three to be colonel in command of a regiment!"

Custer himself wrote his friend, the influential Judge Christiancy, to ask his help in securing the coveted appointment. To his sister Lydia Reed, however, he confessed less optimism. "Everyone knows I am a McClellan man. Politicians never forget these things. Father's Democratic politics might disqualify me, too."

CHAPTER

5

Both Judge Bacon and Lieutenant Custer were right in their prophecies. Whatever the reason, Governor Blair did not give Custer the command of the new Michigan regiment. The young officer had little time for disappointment, however. Word had come that General Lee was on the move again. The Army of Northern Virginia was marching swiftly northward, threatening Baltimore and even Washington itself. The Army of the Potomac must race to keep between the enemy and the capital, and it was the cavalry's job to spearhead the advance.

Custer had no time, either, to write home the stunning news which came to him on June 25, 1863, but the press seized upon it at once. Newspapers always came early to the Humphrey House, and, after one amazed glance, Nettie rushed to her friend's home. Libbie opened the door for her.

"Libbie!" Nettie cried, too full of her tidings to notice how red Libbie's eyes were. "Have you heard the news about Autie?"

To Nettie's surprise Libbie drew back, lifting her chin. "I'm not interested in *any* news of Lieutenant Custer," she declared. "All is over between us. I don't want to hear anything more from him ever again, Nettie. He's a trifler and a flirt." Suddenly her lips trembled and she hid her face in her hands.

Nettie stared, bewildered. "Whatever do you mean?" she asked.

"Fanny Fifield came to see me this morning," Libbie told her. "She said that Armstrong asked for her picture before he left and that they were corresponding. She said, too, that he had shown *my* ambrotype to her, along with those of many other girls!"

"That Fanny!" Annette exclaimed indignantly. "Do you believe her fibs? I've heard her boast the same way about every boy in town, even Jacob Greene, and I certainly know *that* isn't true. Oh Libbie, don't condemn Autie without giving him a chance to explain!"

"But he *did* take Fanny home from singing school last winter," Libbie reminded her.

"Only because your father wouldn't let him take you! Why Libbie, I remember that you yourself suggested it might be a good idea for him to escort some other girl, to stop people from gossiping about you two."

Libbie hesitated. "Yes, I remember that," she admitted. "But I never wanted him to take Fanny. Anyone but her. You know how she flaunts herself. I think that if the truth were told we'd have to admit that Fanny isn't quite—quite a *lady*," she finished, with sudden vehemence.

"That she isn't!" loyal Nettie assured her. "So don't worry. Autie will explain things, I know he will, as soon as I write him what she has said. Now don't you want to hear the news I brought?"

Libbie's face had cleared and she wiped her eyes. "Do you

have a letter there behind you? Is he coming home again on leave?" Libbie asked, full of eagerness once more.

Nettie shook her head. "No, but Libbie, he's been promoted. He's been made a *general!*"

It was Libbie's turn to stare. "A general!" she echoed. Then, smiling indulgently, she shook her head. "No, Nettie, he couldn't be made a general. You don't understand how the ranks go in the Army. From lieutenant he could be made a captain, then a major, then a lieutenant colonel, then a colonel. All those ranks come in between a lieutenant and a general. It's wonderful that he's been promoted, but you must mean that he's been made a captain again."

"No, a *general,*" Nettie insisted. She drew the folded newspaper from behind her back and spread it out. "See, it's there on the first page in black and white. As of June 20th he's a Brigadier General in command of the Second Brigade, Third Division, Cavalry Corps, Army of the Potomac."

Libbie read, caught her breath, read again, then looked up, pale and round-eyed. "It's true!" she whispered. "General Custer! How wonderful it sounds. General Custer!"

Much later Libbie was to learn how the news had come to the young lieutenant. On June 25, at the close of a long day of marching at top speed through pelting rain, the task of inspecting the pickets around the camp had been assigned to Custer and he rode off wearily through the wet dusk. With that duty over he dismounted at last in front of the tent where General Pleasanton's aides were gathered. As he stooped under the tent-flap he heard someone whisper his name. "Here he comes now," another said, and then a chorus of voices greeted him. "Good evening, General Custer."

Too tired and stiff to have much relish for joking, he was about to make a sharp reply, but before he could speak his friend George Yates broke in. "Congratulations, General!" he said.

Suddenly Custer recalled that a few days ago he and his fellow aides had been discussing Pleasanton's elevation to Major-General and complaining that their own promotions were so slow. He himself, he remembered, had been rash enough to boast a little. "Well, I'll bet you that I'll be a general myself if this war keeps up long enough." Now his friends were undoubtedly making fun of him over it. "All right, you fellows," he said, grinning. "Have your joke if you want to. I still say that the way this war is dragging along I'll be a general before it's over. We all will, I reckon."

"Look on the table, Autie," George Yates said.

A large envelope lay there before him. He picked it up and then stiffened, staring at the address. "Brigadier General George Armstrong Custer, U.S. Volunteers," he read. Inside was his commission signed by the Secretary of War.

His knees gave way under him and he sat down so heavily that the flimsy camp chair creaked under him. A dryness filled his throat and for a dreadful moment he thought he was going to burst into tears. "What does it mean?" he asked. His voice came out with difficulty and it sounded hoarse and cracked. "Brigadier General! There must be some mistake. I—I'm only twenty-three!"

"It means what it says," Lieutenant Yates assured him. "Farnsworth and Merritt have been made Brigadier Generals, too. It looks like the Army has discovered at last that it needs more cavalry and officers to command it."

"There's more news, too," another man said. "Hooker is out and General George Meade is now commanding the Army of the Potomac."

"You new generals will have to show that you're worth

your stars, and pretty soon, too," a third added. "A dispatch has just come in. Lee is in Pennsylvania."

There was no time to secure a uniform that would show Custer's new rank, so his orderly, Joseph Fought, set to work to find something to serve for the time being. Luckily, generals did not have to wear regulation uniforms, and they often designed their own. Fought managed to assemble from various sources—from shops in the small town near the camp, from Army supplies and even from a Navy gunboat in the James— a costume which delighted his boyish leader. Attired in a black velveteen jacket with five loops of gold braid on each sleeve, a dark blue shirt with each of its wide collar tabs sewn with a gold star, a bright red silk scarf, high-topped boots and a broad-brimmed black hat set at a rakish angle on his long yellow hair, the new general rode out to inspect his brigade for the first time.

The newspaper reporters, quick to seize on any colorful item, filled their columns with stories of the youngest general the Army had had since Lafayette. "A boy General with golden locks," one of them styled him, and the name stuck. At last the North had a cavalry leader as spectacular in appearance, at least, as the Confederate Jeb Stuart. It remained to be seen how he would compare in battle, as he rode swiftly northward leading his Michigan brigade in the van of Meade's Army. They were headed for a town in Pennsylvania with a name that would go echoing down into history like a roll of drums— Gettysburg.

During that grim three-day encounter, quickly changing orders shifted Custer's Michigan Brigade back and forth on the outskirts of the massive infantry and artillery battle. On July 2 he had a sharp but indecisive clash with a part of Jeb Stuart's cavalry. His horse was shot from under him in a charge and he came out of the fighting mounted behind one of his troopers.

On the afternoon of July 3 the Confederate infantry under General Pickett made a gallant and historic charge which almost swept the South to victory. At the same time four brigades of Stuart's horsemen attempted an assault around the right flank of the Union line in an effort to reach Meade's rear, cut his communications and so demoralize the Northern Army in the moment of crisis.

Four brigades of Northern cavalry, including Custer's, were gathered to block his way. Three times Custer led his regiments in charges. Three times his wild bugle-ring of a shout *"Come on, you Wolverines!"* and the sight of him spurring and swinging his sabre before them set his troopers on fire. They would follow that yellow-haired demon wherever he led! When darkness fell the Confederate cavalry withdrew. Pickett's infantry, too, had failed, and Gettysburg was a hard-won Union victory.

During the days when the Monroe papers were full of the appalling carnage at Gettysburg, Libbie waited, shaken and heartsick, for news of her soldier. She knew that Nettie had written him of her jealousy over Fanny's claims. "How terrible if that should be the last message he ever received from me!" she thought. Every night she prayed desperately that she might be granted another sight of him, and then lay staring with hot eyes into the darkness, wondering if she would ever again hear his eager footfall on her steps.

At last came a letter dated two weeks after the battle. It was hurriedly written at a brief halt to feed horses and to give the men a chance to eat. "Tell Libbie that Fanny has nothing in her power to bestow that would have induced me to show her that ambrotype. I know nothing of what representations of our intimacy she has made to Libbie. It is no different from what I told her. I would write more but must mount and away. Please tell my sister I am well."

Later, in another letter he went further. Nettie had evidently spared nothing of what Libbie had said. "When the time comes for me to give her up, I hope it will find me the same soldier I now try to be, capable of meeting the reverses of life as well as of war." Libbie read injured, boyish pride in the words, but at least he was safe! That's all that truly matters, she told herself. If I have hurt him I'll make it up to him. Oh, I promise I will. If—she added, with a cold shiver of fear— if I have the chance. He isn't safe yet, not really safe ever, so long as this war lasts.

The message Nettie's next letter carried from Libbie was warm enough to please any lover. When he replied it was in his former gay style, describing the fine food he was enjoying at his headquarters in Virginia. He told, too, of the staff he had at last had time to assemble. Nettie's young man, Captain Jacob Greene, was his adjutant and George Yates was an aide too. Besides his orderly, Fought, he had a boy named Johnny Cisco to look after his horses and dogs.

He also had a cook! A well-mannered colored woman had arrived at his camp one morning with the news that she had been a slave and had decided that she didn't want to sit down and wait to be freed, but would like to help free herself by helping the Yankees win the War. She was a good cook and as brave under fire as any soldier, Custer reported. He gave her a captured carriage in which to pack her cooking pots and supplies, with a pair of decrepit cavalry horses to pull it, and she was always on hand whenever mealtime came with good hot food for her "Ginnel." The men called her "The Queen of Sheba."

"What did Judge Bacon think of the promotion?" Armstrong added. "Did he approve, or did he maintain a dignified silence?"

In September Libbie and her parents were visiting in Traverse City when the papers told of Custer leading a charge against a Confederate battery at Culpepper Station and capturing several cannon. He also captured Jeb Stuart's headquarters and with it that General's uneaten dinner!

"The Boy General's horse was killed under him and he himself suffered a wound," the paper continued.

"A wound!" Libbie could not restrain her tears.

Judge Bacon looked grieved and concerned. "Now, Libbie, you'll surely see how right I am in protecting you from risking your future happiness with a soldier," he told her. But Libbie only cried harder and would not answer him.

Mrs. Bacon decided to visit relatives in Clinton, so Libbie and her father boarded again at the Humphrey House. At her first opportunity Libbie hurried to Nettie's room. "Have you any news? Is his wound serious?" she asked.

"It's only a slight flesh-wound in the leg," Nettie answered. "And oh, Libbie, he's been given a sick leave because of it. Twenty-five days. He'll be here any time now."

All Monroe competed to honor and entertain the wounded hero, the Boy General who had brought fame to their town, but Custer lost no time in arranging, through Annette, a meeting with Libbie. "You *do* love me and we will be married at once!" he declared, taking her into his arms.

She nodded against his chest. "Yes, I'm yours forever and ever," she answered.

"I'll go and see your father," he told her. "Will he be at home today?"

"Give me a little time to break the news to him," Libbie

begged. "I'm sure he likes and admires you, but he is still afraid for me to marry a soldier. Perhaps tomorrow?"

The Judge listened to Libbie's confession soberly. He did not show anger, only deep regret. "A brigadier general is in a far more vulnerable position than a lieutenant, especially if, like Custer, he insists upon leading his men in their charges. However, I promise to give the matter my earnest thought."

The next morning, to Libbie's consternation, he told her that business called him to Traverse City. "But General Custer was to call this afternoon!" she protested.

"Pray make my excuses to him. I prefer not to be hurried into a decision so momentous to us all."

General Custer, who had charged fearlessly into enemy batteries, now found himself baffled and helpless before the old lawyer. The Judge remained away until the evening before the young officer's leave ended. That night Libbie stood before her father, trembling but determined. "Armstrong and I are engaged to be married," she said. "We will not announce it until you give permission, but I love him and will love him until I die. Nothing can change that. He is leaving tomorrow and I shall go down to the station to see him off. I should like you to come with me, but I shall go whether you come or not."

"I will come with you, Elizabeth," he answered. "You know it is quite unthinkable for you to go alone."

At the station he shook hands cordially with Custer and complimented him on his past exploits. But when the young man tried to break in with what was filling his heart, the Judge maneuvered the conversation quickly to a different subject.

At last, with the train clanging into the station, Custer blurted out "I have tried to speak to you alone. We both know

what I mean. Since there has been no opportunity for that,
I shall write."

"Very well," Judge Bacon replied. He had kept a firm grip
on Libbie's arm, and when she made an impulsive step forward
he drew her back. The lovers could only look at one another,
gray eyes into blue. Then he was gone, the plume of smoke
from the train fading into the sky.

Libbie was to read in the papers of more battles and perils
for her general before her father finally answered Custer's
letters, and gave his consent to their engagement. At once
Custer began to write directly to Libbie, impetuous, ardent
letters urging that they be married as soon as he could get
another leave.

By the rules of etiquette young ladies of that day were supposed to show a modest reluctance toward marriage, and Libbie's replies reflected that custom. They were warm and
loving, but marriage, so soon? "If I am worth having am I not
worth waiting for?" she wrote. "The very thought of marriage makes me tremble. Girls have such fun! If you tease me
I will go into a convent for a year. The very thought of leaving home is painful to me. I implore you not to mention it for
at least a year."

Her coquetry had no effect upon the young man except to
make him urge her the more. Then, to Libbie's utter surprise,
her father began to accuse her of trifling. "My dear, you must
not keep Armstrong waiting," he told her. And when Custer
sent a tinted portrait of himself for Libbie's Christmas present,
the Judge hung it in her room while she was out to surprise her.

At last, in December, it was settled. They would be married
when he came home on leave in February. In the meantime,
Libbie wrote that she had had a glimpse of his family—they
had stood near each other at a bazaar. Now that the wedding-

day was set she and Nettie were going to call on Mrs. Reed and
on the Custer parents, who had recently bought a house and
moved to Monroe.

Bundled in furs, Nettie and Libbie crossed snowy Monroe
Street and walked the short distance under the bare-limbed
trees to the Reed home. "Whatever does one talk about on an
occasion like this?" Libbie asked nervously. "I haven't been
so frightened since I was valedictorian at the seminary!"

"Don't worry. Lydia Reed is a darling, and she'll make you
feel at home right away," Nettie assured her.

Armstrong's sister welcomed them at the door. "Come in,
come in out of the cold," she urged, and without any other
formality, took Libbie into her arms, gave her a hug and
kissed her. "You are all that Autie described," she laughed.
"No wonder *I* don't get such long letters from him any more."

The children were lined up, scrubbed and shining, each
with a kiss for "Aunt Libbie." The youngest, named Armstrong after his uncle, hung his head, too shy to look at her.
He let himself be kissed, however, and after that stayed glued
to her side. The visit was a great success. Libbie described it
in glowing terms to her parents on her return and to Armstrong in her next letter.

Then came the call on the Custer parents. The Judge and
Mrs. Bacon accompanied her there. Mr. Custer, erect, bearded,
and blue-eyed like his son, was full of jokes. "You're getting
the best of boys for a husband," he told Libbie. "Everyone
says he takes after me, eh, Mother?" and he laughed up-
roariously.

His gentle little wife tugged at his sleeve. "Now Emmanuel!
You'll frighten poor Libbie. She's not used to your ways.
Don't pay any mind to him, my dear."

"Well, Mr. Custer, I think you'll get to like our Libbie,

too," the Judge said. "That is, after you know her better," he added, with a teasing twinkle in his eye.

Glowing with happiness, Libbie gave her father a grateful look. How foolish she had been to dread this meeting! She had feared it might be a stiff one, knowing how different the two men were in every way. Once the Judge had yielded, however, he seemed wholehearted and generous in his approval. Now there was not a single flaw in her joy.

To her cousin Rebecca Richmond Libbie sent the news of her coming marriage. "Oh Rebecca, it is beyond words blissful to love and to be loved!" The wedding day was set for February 9. "I am going to Detroit to have my dresses made, and my underclothes will be made on the machine. I am sending to New York for my silks."

CHAPTER

6

The next month was crowded full to the brim for Libbie with shopping trips, dressmaker's fittings, invitation lists, consultations with her bridesmaids and, always, long letters to Armstrong. The wedding was set for Tuesday, February 9, 1864 at eight o'clock in the evening, in the brick Presbyterian Church. The Reverend Dr. Boyd was to perform the ceremony, assisted by the Reverend Mr. Matson, minister of the church.

For bridesmaids Libbie chose, first of all, Annette Humphrey, of course, then Ann Darrah and Marie Miller. Custer's groomsmen were to be his adjutant, Captain Jacob Greene, Conway Noble, who had introduced him to Libbie, and a boyhood friend, John Bulkeley.

It would take Custer three days to travel from Virginia to Monroe. Libbie learned with dismay that in order to arrive on Monday he would have to travel on Sunday! Strict keeping of the Sabbath was part of her religious training and it troubled her conscience even to write letters on that day. "Still, if it brings you here a day sooner—" She finally conceded. "And why is it worse to write to you than to spend the day dreaming about you?" she found herself reasoning.

In spite of the snow and biting cold, a crowd gathered at the Monroe station to watch the arrival of the celebrated general and his staff, brilliant in their uniforms of blue and gold. Private Tom Custer, Armstrong's younger brother, had obtained leave to attend his brother's wedding and had joined the party on the train. It was their first meeting in several years and the reunion added to the noisy hilarity of the journey.

After a brief call at the elder Custer's house the high-spirited group walked around the block to the Bacon home. At first glimpse of them rounding the corner Libbie fled up the stairs "to fetch a handkerchief" she explained hurriedly to a few guests who had dropped in to view the wedding gifts. She could hear the sound of booted feet on the porch and then the quiet house was suddenly full of young men's voices and their laughter. She peered into the mirror, smoothing her hair with hands that felt cold and had begun to tremble.

How pale I look! she thought. Really haggard. Oh dear, everyone said I was working too hard over the wedding preparations, and now it shows. Will *he* be disappointed?

Then, above the other sounds, she heard his voice. "Where's Libbie? All these presents are very fine, but I want to see my girl!"

Warmth rushed through her. She could feel color afire in her cheeks as she ran down the stairs and into his arms, where his hug swung her off the floor. His coat was frosty-cold from the out-of-doors and his face felt rough and chilly against hers, but it was plain that he was not disappointed.

Arm in arm they walked about viewing the display of wedding gifts in the room just off the parlor. From the regiments of his brigade had come a beautiful silver dinner-service and tea-set. Among the most interesting and unique items, Libbie pointed out two white silk fans with sandalwood sticks, a mosaic chess stand and several richly bound books, *Mrs. Browning's Poems,* a collection entitled *Female Poets* and another *Whispers To A Bride.*

"My parents gave me this beautiful gold watch and this Bible," Libbie told him. "And my mother picked out as her special gift to me this white silk parasol covered with black lace. Oh Armstrong, aren't they all lovely?"

"Yes, they're really beautiful. But I'm wondering how we're going to get them all into my tent," Custer said, and shook his head in mock dismay.

In a letter to her sister Mary, who had not been able to come to the wedding, Rebecca Richmond sent home a description of the festivities. Libbie had rushed out to greet her on her arrival, as unaffected and natural as her old school-girl self, not a bit changed by the fact that she would soon be the wife of a famous general. Rebecca reported herself agreeably surprised in Custer. From the accounts in the papers she had expected him to be foppish and conceited, but he was a simple, frank, manly fellow.

Rebecca thought the wedding itself a beautiful ceremony. The bridesmaids wore white tarlatan and the groomsmen and bridegroom wore their dress uniforms, as did the other members of Custer's staff who attended. Libbie's dress was of white corded silk, rich and heavy enough to "walk into church alone." It was made with "an extensive trail" and a bertha of point lace. Her lace veil was held in place by orange blossoms, and it floated clear to the floor, covering her train.

After describing the wedding presents to her sister, Rebecca assured her that Libbie's trousseau was "rich and in fine taste." Her traveling dress was of dark brown "empress cloth." Her "hotel sacque" was of the same with white buttons, a "jaunty little thing." Her hat, of the same shade, had a blue velvet facing. She had a waterproof coat with armholes, buttoned from head to foot in case of bad weather. In all she had nine silk dresses, among them a "double dress" of lilac silk faced and trimmed with plaid, a breakfast dress of light blue merino scalloped and bound with black velvet, a brown silk dress, a light green silk dress striped in a darker shade "very richly trimmed," a riding dress of dark green trimmed with brass buttons. Her dress hat was of lavender velvet trimmed with a white feather, her opera cloak of white merino lined with silk and there was also a silk hood with "rich tassels."

The church was crowded to overflowing and there were three hundred guests at the reception afterwards at the Bacon house. It was said to be the most splendid wedding ever held in the state of Michigan! After the reception, the four couples of the wedding party changed to traveling clothes and took the midnight train for Cleveland. That night, those left at home were kept awake by fears that burglars might steal the wedding gifts. Next morning "Uncle Bacon" packed them up and took them to the bank.

In Cleveland the Custers were guests of honor at a reception and a gay party afterwards, given by Mr. Chares Noble. The next day bride and groom embarked for Buffalo. Libbie shed a few tears at parting from her bridesmaids, but they soon dried. It was impossible to be low-spirited when it was such fun to be married, and married to a famous general, so admired and sought after. Gentlemen who were perfect strangers to them came up and spoke to Armstrong in the hotel lobby or at the railroad station to express their admiration. "If we had more generals like you, this war would have been over long ago," one man declared, shaking him by the hand.

Libbie marveled at the poise and grave dignity with which her young husband received all this attention, especially when, alone with her, he became a different person entirely—a gay-hearted boy as well as the most ardent of lovers. The world was dazzlingly bright. Marriage to the man she loved was pure bliss. The War was so far away that it hardly seemed to exist for Libbie Bacon Custer.

The young couple visited Libbie's relatives along the way, and Libbie was able to show off her trousseau before loudly admiring aunts, cousins and friends. At one time they were in the midst of the display when train time came and the porter arrived for their trunks. Then there was a mad scramble to pack the things again. Even the General was enlisted to help and managed to get himself comically entangled in a hoop-skirt. All the party hurried to the station and helped them aboard. Hanging out of the train window, Libbie snatched off her husband's hat to wave goodbye and the band fell off it. One of the young boy-cousins had to sprint beside the moving train to hand it back again.

At Howlett's Hill, New York, the Sabin relatives held open house in their honor. Relatives came from near and far and ad-mirers of the General swelled their numbers. In the evening they danced to the music of Cousin George's fiddle under the rafters of the big kitchen. "None of these new-fangled slow-poke waltzes for us!" Uncle George called. "Strike up a good old tune that will give us some action!"

George swung into the vigorous rhythm of "Money Musk" and the couples formed for the square dance. Custer entered so enthusiastically into the fun that Libbie's feet seemed never to touch the floor. At last she gave out entirely and sank to the ground, helpless with laughter at the sight of her uncle and aunt still bounding tirelessly through the figures.

On they traveled toward New York, with a stopover at West Point where Custer had graduated less than three years before. From the train they could see the snowy, tree-darkened hills and highlands on the west bank of the Hudson. The rugged scenery seemed dramatically beautiful to Libbie, after the flat Erie country. The cliffs towered higher and steeper above the river as they neared the Academy and Custer pointed out where the old forts had stood during the Revolution, where a chain had been stretched from shore to shore to keep the British gunboats off, and also Buttermilk Falls, where famous Benny Havens kept his inn. He told Libbie stories of his own years at West Point and of some of his best friends and classmates, who were now in the Confederate Army.

One night he and a comrade had swum the Hudson River with their clothes tied on their heads in bundles to attend a dinner on the opposite shore. In spite of their precautions, however, their clothes had got too wet for them to appear with the other guests, and they had had to stay in the barn where a servant kindly brought them food.

"You swam that great river!" Libbie exclaimed. "Oh Autie, however could you dare!"

When they alighted from the train opposite West Point they found that the Hudson was frozen so solid that the ferry had stopped running. Libbie looked across at the Academy buildings high on a shelf of the mountain wall. "What a disappointment," she mourned. "What a pity we even got off the train, Autie."

"Nonsense," he told her. "I'm not going to have my bride disappointed in anything."

He left her inside the shelter of the small station for a few minutes, then returned with a tall farm boy pulling a sled. "Get aboard, Libbie. The Express Stage for the Point is about to take off!"

Bundled against the piercing wind, pulled by the farm boy and pushed by Autie, Libbie crossed the frozen river on the ice. At the Academy the famous graduate was the center of attention. Even the dogs seemed to remember him! A professor who had taught Custer in his classes insisted upon welcoming his bride with a kiss, and several upper-classmen vied for the honor of showing the lovely, smiling visitor about the grounds.

They returned across the river and resumed their train journey. Bubbling with delight over their reception, Libbie was surprised to get no response from her husband. He had slid down into his seat and was scowling out of the window. "Whatever is the matter?" she asked.

"Matter? Did you expect me to *like* seeing you kissing one man and flirting with a dozen others?" he demanded. "On our honeymoon?"

She could not believe her ears. Autie jealous? "But the professor was as old as Methuselah and those cadets were just sweet, clean, friendly boys."

"Sweet boys! I was a cadet myself not so long ago. *I* know those blasted young devils!"

Libbie clapped her hands over her ears. "Autie!" she gasped. "You swore at me! How could you?" And she buried her face in her handkerchief.

At once he was all contrition and apology. "Libbie, my darling, don't cry. Forgive me, my dearest. The words just slipped out. Oh please don't cry!"

She lifted tear-wet eyes. "Very well, I will forgive you, but only because I love you so much. You must remember, though, that you yourself left me alone with those cadets, Autie," and she rested her head once again in its special place against his shoulder. Quarreling was terrible, Libbie decided, but making up afterwards was such fun that it was almost worth it.

In New York they stayed at the Metropolitan Hotel, where Custer had lived during his work on General McClellan's reports. Once again the "Boy General" was the center of admiration and his young wife glowed with pride. They attended a performance of the famous play, "Uncle Tom's Cabin," and Libbie laughed and cried without restraint over the humor and the pathos.

"I'm so glad that you like the theatre too, darling. When we get to Washington we'll go often," Armstrong promised her. "All the best shows come there. There'll be parties and receptions and concerts, too. The 'Hops' at the National Hotel are especially gay. Everyone seems to be dancing, nowadays. How proud I'll be to show off my beautiful bride!"

Libbie's first sight of Washington, however, was bleakly disappointing. They arrived in a cold, sleety downpour and the broad streets and avenues were rivers of mud and slush. The cab in which they drove from the station to their hotel was caught in a jam of carts, carriages and army wagons, and for a time it seemed as if they would never move again. When they finally arrived, Custer had to carry her across the flooded gutter and sidewalk into the hotel.

The lobby was large and gorgeous, but it was crowded and noisy and blue with cigar smoke. Libbie waited, sitting nervously on the edge of a plush-covered chair for her husband to arrange for their luggage and their rooms, conscious that she was being stared at so boldly by insolent-appearing men that finally she did not dare to lift her eyes from her lap. One of them even attempted to speak to her! Fortunately Custer joined her at that moment and the fellow disappeared hastily into the throng.

"What sort of a place is this, Autie?" she whispered, cling-

ing to his arm as they climbed the stairs to their rooms. "Some
of those women—I'm sure they are wearing powder and rouge!"

"It's the best hotel in the city, darling," he assured her. "Do
you think I'd take you anywhere else? As for those women—"
He paused, frowning. "Even some of the most elegant and
fashionable ladies in Washington do use some makeup. They
aren't blessed with your lovely complexion, darling. Forget
about them, Libbie. How do you like our rooms?"

She looked about at the sumptuous elegance of plush and
marble and walnut. "It's beautiful," she said. "Much too grand
for your little country wife, Autie."

"Nothing's too good for my beautiful Elizabeth," he assured
her, and all seemed well with the world again.

Almost before they had time to take off their wraps there
was a knock at the door. "This telegram was waiting for you,
General," the bellboy said.

Custer opened it and frowned as he read it. "I'm ordered to
report at once to my brigade's encampment in Virginia," he
said. "Darling, they've cut my leave short! I'll have to start in
the morning. But first I'll find a comfortable place for you here
in Washington, Libbie. Not in this hotel but at a place that has
been recommended to me. Miss Hyatt's boarding house is cen-
trally located, right on Pennsylvania Avenue, and the wives of
several officers whom I know are staying there."

"Stay in Washington without you?" Libbie faltered. "Oh
Autie, no! Let me come to the camp with you. You told me
you'd let me visit you there, and why not begin now? I won't
mind roughing it; it will be fun! *Do* let me. I have a riding habit
and you promised to give me lessons."

How could a young man in love refuse when his bride begged
so hard? "Very well," he conceded at last. "So you want to become a little Army crow? I'll take you there for a while, at least,

just to show you what it's like. But remember, the first word of complaint and back you go!"

"I shan't complain!" Libbie promised, lifting her chin in the spirited way he had come to adore. "If I can be with you, Autie, nothing else matters."

Custer's Brigade Headquarters was at Stevensburg, Virginia, a few miles from Brandy Station, scene of one of his fights. He settled Libbie in a farmhouse owned by a Southern couple who were too thankful to be allowed to keep their home to show resentment. His cook, Eliza, was brought to wait upon her. Libbie sent cheerful, enthusiastic letters to her parents describing her new life. They had traveled here by train, she wrote. To meet them at the station, instead of a converted army ambulance such as most of the Army wives used, Custer had a comfortable captured carriage drawn by a pair of matched horses with silver-mounted harness. An escort of six soldiers rode behind them.

On Sundays a regimental chaplain held services and the band played hymn tunes. She had had several riding lessons and Autie complimented her on her progress. She did not write that the enemy was only ten or twelve miles away from them on the Rapidan River, nor that she had barely been installed when Armstrong was ordered out on a raid!

Less than three weeks after her marriage, Libbie found herself standing on the porch of the Virginia farmhouse to watch her husband mount and take his place at the head of his men. He had said his goodbyes to her. Now, erect in the saddle he looked down at her once more with only the briefest of bright glances, then faced forward. A gauntleted hand on the reins held his horse in check while the highbred animal danced under him. Libbie's heart pounded in her throat and her breath came fast. How beautiful they both are together! she thought. Two superb, spirited creatures moving as one. It seemed to her that the very air about them vibrated with their overflowing energy and eagerness to be off.

He lifted his hand in signal and a trumpet blared out a command. He was riding away into she could only guess what danger. It took all of her resolution to hold her head high and to keep a smile on her lips while she watched the mile-long line of troopers who followed him ride by. The February wind pierced even through her warm shawl, but she stayed until the last rider had clattered and jingled past. Her only sight of cavalry before this had been on parades. How different these men looked now, burdened with their equipment, their blanket-rolls and arms! But they rode with a swing and a dash behind their young leader, nevertheless, proudly flaunting the red neck-scarfs which Autie had made famous.

The shadows were long as the winter sun moved toward the horizon, and the mud churned up by the many hoofs was beginning to freeze. Dusk would come soon and then night. Autie was gone. She was alone in this bleak Virginia landscape, almost in enemy country. How much could she trust the couple whose home it was? A detail of soldiers had been left behind to guard her, it was true, and there was Eliza.

Libbie turned toward the door. She had been standing still for so long that her feet were numb with the cold and she stumbled. Gratefully she caught Eliza's outstretched hand to steady herself, then, with a sob, accepted the shelter of her arms.

"Never you fear, Miss Libbie," the woman crooned in her rich, soft voice. "The Ginnel always comes back. 'Custer luck,' the men calls it. Nothin' can touch *him*."

Alone in the big four-poster bed Libbie lay awake for a long time. When she fell asleep at last it was to start up again, sobbing and shivering with fear and cold. "I had such a dream!" she told the solicitous Eliza. "It was about Autie, but it was all mixed up with some nightmares I used to have when I was a little girl. He was in terrible danger, not from Rebels, but from *Indians!* Indians, like those in the Raisin River battle. Imagine that!" Libbie laughed shakily. "What ridiculous things dreams are!"

The days and nights dragged slowly. Libbie had no more such nightmares, but the haunting fear was never absent. It seemed to have become a part of her body, a heavy coldness always present just below her heart. War, which had seemed so unreal and remote, was now all about her. Was this to be the pattern of her life now and forever, this endless, agonized waiting? But I shan't complain, she vowed. At least I'll be able to see him far oftener here than if I were in Washington.

Then one evening there was the sound of galloping hoofs, the door banged open, and his voice rang through the house. "Where's my girl?" She was in his arms and all her misery and fears were blown away like fog in a great fresh wind. He was unshaven, hollow-eyed, haggard, mudspattered—dirtier than any man she had ever been near before—but he was hers again. His mission, a raid on Chancellorsville, had been accomplished with triumphant success and he had ridden more than a hundred miles in two days just to be with her. No one in all the world was ever so gloriously happy as she!

For the next few weeks Custer was able to devote much of his time to Libbie. General Webb and General Pleasanton both gave dinners at their headquarters in their honor, and the young couple drove there in their carriage and prancing pair. The Webbs lived in a charming series of little huts opening into each other and surrounded by evergreens, and built for them by the soldiers. General Pleasanton's elaborate six-course dinner was served with wines appropriate for each course, but Libbie wrote proudly to her father that Autie refused them all.

By the end of March the roads in Virginia began to dry out. With the mud gone, preparations started for a great spring campaign, and Custer's headquarters would no longer be in one settled spot. Libbie must return to Washington.

They boarded a special train which had been routed through to the Capital to carry a new commander whom President Lincoln had called from his victories in the West to lead the Army of the Potomac, General Ulysses S. Grant. General and Mrs. Custer were introduced, and Libbie thought him oddly undistinguished and unassuming for so famous a man. He was short, his hair was sandy, and his eyes greenish-blue. He was pleasant and affable, however, and seemed glad to talk to the pretty bride, the only woman on the train. He soon set her at ease with his funny stories. Libbie, responding, remembered that the general was reported to be a fine horseman and complimented him upon it.

"Oh yes, a small officer always likes to be seen on horseback," he answered with a genial grin. "And small men, Mrs. Custer, invariably ride horses seventeen hands high!"

Then he excused himself and went out on the platform to smoke a cigar. "If he's out there among the cinders just because he fears his smoking will be disagreeable to me, please tell him that I don't mind a bit, Autie. Beg him to come back," Libbie asked. Whereupon the General returned gratefully and smoked five more cigars during the journey.

Before reporting again for duty Custer was able to take his young wife to Baltimore, where they enjoyed a visit to the theatre to see the popular comedian, Clarke. The city of Baltimore looked truly elegant to Libbie, much like New York with its brownstone fronts and white steps. They saw Joseph Jefferson in *Rip Van Winkle* when they returned to the capital, but the city, even Pennsylvania Avenue, still seemed sprawling and untidy to Libbie and the streets were still full of mud. Wagons were often mired down in bog-holes on all but the few cobbled pavements.

Autie pointed out the stubby, unfinished shaft honoring Washington that would someday tower above the city he had founded. They visited the Capitol where the bronze statute of Freedom had just been put in place above the huge dome. The area was still littered with piles of brick and lumber, workmen's huts and scaffolding, but the inside was beautiful and elegant. Libbie was shocked, however, by the "wrangling" she heard in the House of Representatives.

Custer's promotion to Brigadier General had just been confirmed by Congress. When it was reported that he was in the city he was invited to the floor of the House and surrounded by members eager to congratulate him on his recent raid on Chancellorsville, for the newspapers were full of this latest of his exploits. A picture of him leading a charge adorned the front cover of *Harpers' Weekly* and, the next week, a two-page spread in the center of the magazine depicted drawings of the raid.

Libbie, too, received her share of compliments. Senators Wade and Chandler asked her to save dances for them if she attended any of the "hops" held every Thursday evening at the National Hotel. Libbie accepted graciously, although both gallants seemed so elderly to her that she could barely suppress her laughter at the thought of them as beaux.

When Armstrong was presented formally to the President, Lincoln told him that he had been following his career with great interest. Libbie's letters carried all this news back to Monroe. Washington was going to be very agreeable and homelike, she wrote brightly. She already had made many friends at Miss Hyatt's boarding house, and her room was attractive and comfortable.

Her own thoughts were far less cheerful. To be separated from Autie again, and so soon!

CHAPTER

7

When Libbie entered the dining room of the boarding house on her first evening alone, Miss Hyatt came fluttering to greet her. "My dear Mrs. Custer!" she exclaimed. "All my guests are waiting eagerly to meet you. Your famous husband has been so much in the news that we feel honored to have you among us."

Libbie murmured appreciative thanks and the plump spinster then proceeded to lead her around the table and introduce the other boarders in turn. Miss Hyatt, for all her elaborate curls and furbelows, was far from young. She must be at least forty! Libbie thought. But even so she's younger than most of the people here, she added, her heart sinking. The two ladies whose officer-husbands Autie knew were handsome and well-dressed, but they were surely middle-aged, while the man beside whom Miss Hyatt finally seated Libbie had a white beard which reached halfway to his waist.

"I'm entrusting our little bride to your care, Professor Harris," Miss Hyatt told him. "Even the most doting of young husbands could not be jealous of so eminent a Greek scholar," she added, with an arch, tinkling laugh.

The Professor bowed, seated himself again, and peered at Libbie over his spectacles with eyes that were surprisingly bright and twinkling. "Don't be too sure, Miss Hyatt," he answered. "A man may have white hair but still be charmed by beauty. If you will recall your Iliad, Mrs. Custer, you will remember that in Book III it was the *old* men, sitting on the tower at the Skaian gates, chattering like grasshoppers in the sun, who first noticed Helen as she came walking along the wall in her shining robes. They watched her as she came and remarked to each other that it was small wonder the Trojans and Greeks alike should suffer years of war for her sake. No, age does not alter the appreciation of loveliness. I thank the good Lord for that!"

The Iliad had not been on the course of study at Boyd's Seminary, but Libbie had been well enough schooled in other matters to know how to respond to an old gentleman's gallantry. She smiled, dropped her long lashes, then looked up again with wide eyes. "It must be wonderful to have a mind so stored with learning!" she said. "How I regret my own ignorance." The Professor is old but I *do* like him, she decided. He's going to be fun to talk to. And Autie can't possibly mind if I flirt a little with him, just to keep in practice. Her spirits rose and she found herself eating the dinner set before her with more appetite than she had expected.

General Custer had many friends in Washington and now they rallied about Libbie to keep her from loneliness. With Armstrong's permission, Senator Zacharias Chandler invited her to attend a "hop" at the National Hotel. The other ladies told her that tarlatan gowns were the mode for dancing, and so Libbie got herself a new dress. When the evening came she glided into the ballroom on the distinguished Senator's arm in a froth of palest blue. The hall was crowded. Civilians in formal black-and-white and officers in blue and gold made a background for the rainbow-hued, full-skirted gowns of the ladies and for the sparkle of jewels that adorned white arms, necks, and bosoms.

"Now watch while the young fellows crowd up to ask for introductions to the prettiest woman here," the Senator said. "But I'm keeping your program card safely in *my* possession. I'll give them a chance, but I warn you that I'm saving most of your dances for myself."

In spite of his years the Senator proved to be a skillful dancer and Libbie floated happily through the waltzes, polkas, and schottisches with him and the other partners to whom he granted favors. Libbie loved to dance, the floor was perfect and the music entrancing. The magic and excitement of Autie's presence were sadly lacking, but it was a pleasant way to pass the time, she decided, even though the Senator's compliments grew warmer and the clasp of his arm closer as the evening wore on. Returning home in the carriage he became so sentimental that it took all her smiling tact to ward off his advances without offending the influential statesman.

It was fortunate for the Senator's vanity that he could not know what Libbie wrote home to her father, Judge Bacon. "Father, darling, don't tell, but Mr. Ch. is an old goosey idiot. . . . Oh, so silly!"

On a visit to the theatre with other friends Libbie saw that the box opposite their own was draped with flags. "That means the President is expected," her host told her. Suddenly the orchestra struck up the stirring strains of "Hail to the Chief" and the audience rose to its feet. Libbie felt a surge of anticipation and excitement as several elegantly dressed ladies and gentlemen appeared in the box's dim interior. "There he is!" a voice cried. The audience began to clap and a tall figure bowed several times before seating himself.

Libbie had seen many pictures of Abraham Lincoln, but none had prepared her for the deeply shadowed eyes, the sunken cheeks or the careworn pallor she saw now. Truly it was the face of a man who carried on his shoulders and in his heart burdens far too heavy to bear.

In her own heart Libbie felt a stabbing pain of compassion such as she had never experienced before. Her fears and terrors for her husband, multiplied by the griefs and fears of so many thousands of others like herself, were all loaded together upon the President of a country at war to form the unendurable weight of his lonely, unique responsibility.

Later in April, Representative and Mrs. Kellogg invited the General's young wife to go with them to the President's levee, the last reception at the White House that season. They set out at ten o'clock and their carriage was soon engulfed in a traffic jam which lasted until they reached the steps of the Executive Mansion. Swept forward by the crowd past the guards with their drawn sabres, Libbie found herself first in the cloak room, then in a room papered and furnished in crimson, and finally in the Blue Room where the President and Mrs. Lincoln stood to receive their guests. Libbie was passed along the line and Lincoln's large, white-gloved hand clasped and shook hers automatically. He looked less pale and careworn than at the theatre, she thought, studying the face so far above hers.

She was moving away when suddenly he turned to her again. "Mrs. *Custer?*" he exclaimed. "The wife of our youngest general?" He took her hand once more and this time his face was miraculously changed and illumined by his smile. "So this is the young woman whose husband goes into a charge with a whoop and a shout? Well, after seeing you, my dear, I shan't blame him if he doesn't do so any more."

"Oh, Mr. President, I'm sure he will, as much as ever!" Libbie assured him earnestly. "I would *never* ask him to change."

He threw back his head and laughed. "Then you want to be a widow, I see," he said, but with such a droll inflection that Libbie found herself laughing, too. Then the line was in motion again and she moved with it, her cheeks blazing, her heart beating fast at the unexpected honor his attention had brought her. How everyone admires Autie! she thought, tremulous with happiness and pride.

In the magnificent East Room Libbie met many dignitaries. Among them was the handsome and popular Speaker of the House, Schuyler Colfax. "I have been wishing to be introduced to this young lady ever since she entered the room," he told Representative Kellogg, genially. "What a disappointment to find that she is a Mrs. Ah, well, how can I begrudge his good fortune to our most gallant young general?"

Between such festivities Libbie passed her days in writing to Armstrong and to her parents and friends, in sewing, and in sketching and painting with watercolors. She made friends with the officers' wives who were her fellow-boarders, Mrs. Wooster, an older woman, and especially with the younger, whom she called by her first name, Cara. She had begun to count Professor Harris as a friend too. They often spent the afternoon in Miss Hyatt's pretty garden, she sewing, he reading aloud in his mellow, resonant voice from his translations. Libbie had studied some poetry at school, and had fancied herself well-read, but here was something new to her. She found herself sharing a little of young John Keats' wonder as Homer's sonorous phrases echoed in her ears.

These were only methods of passing the slow-dragging days between the arrival of the letters from the front; letters, however, on which her whole existence now seemed to hang. One of the envelopes was thicker than usual and when she opened it a small packet of yellow hair fell out. "I have shaved off my mustache and imperial," he wrote. (An "imperial" was a tuft of beard on the chin.) "I am sending my mustache to you. My staff say that it changes my appearance so much that you won't know me. But I'm sure I could find ways of making myself known to you!"

Another mail brought her favorite cake sent all the way from Monroe by Mrs. Bacon. Tasting it carried Libbie back to her girlhood and she shed a few homesick tears. That afternoon at teatime she was sharing her cake with Mrs. Wooster when they heard the door burst open and feet pounding up the stairs.

"Good heavens! Is the house afire?" Mrs. Wooster cried, turning pale.

Libbie was far from pale. "It's Autie!" she cried. She sprang up to meet him, then shrank back with a gasp of dismay at sight of the smooth-faced stranger in her doorway. "Autie, is it really you?"

Neither of them noticed that Mrs. Wooster had hurried from the room with a murmured excuse. "Autie, how funny you look!" Libbie exclaimed again. His kisses, too, were strange. Without his mustache and imperial it was like kissing a girl!

He had been given forty-eight hours leave to attend to some matters in Washington for General Sheridan, the new commander Grant had brought in to lead the Cavalry Corps. Forty-eight shining hours, precious as jewels, that were gone, it seemed to Libbie, almost before they had begun. Then she was alone again with the added knowledge heavy upon her that a campaign of battles must soon commence.

Endless trains of army wagons had begun to rumble over the uneven pavements and every day several regiments of infantry of the Army of the Potomac, back from their furloughs, swung past along the Avenue. Each marched to the music of its band, and Libbie and Cara hung out of Libbie's front windows to watch them. Only a block from the boarding house the long lines turned to cross the bridge which led over the river to the blood-soaked soil of Virginia, where the enemy waited!

Early in May Libbie received a letter from Armstrong warning her that communications with Washington would soon be abandoned for a while and that she should not expect any letters. Then once again came days and nights of agonized waiting. Soon the papers carried news of a Union Cavalry raid deep into Southern territory, and an engagement at Yellow Tavern. It was reported that General J. E. B. Stuart had suffered a fatal wound. Custer had led a charge against a battery of enemy cannon.

Now the hospitals began to fill up with wounded brought up from the river-steamers in slow-moving lines of ambulances, and dark, flag-draped funeral corteges passed continually along Washington's streets. Still no word from *him*. Libbie tried to believe what everyone assured her—that no news was good news—yet how could she be certain?

Finally, after almost two weeks of waiting, word came. Armstrong's letter fairly glittered with excitement and exultation. "We have passed through days of carnage and have lost heavily," he wrote. "But we have been successful. The Michigan Brigade has covered itself with undying glory. General Sheridan sent his aide to me on the battlefield with his congratulations. We were inside the fortifications of Richmond at one time. I enclose some honeysuckle plucked there."

Another letter followed soon, in the same vein. "General Sheridan told Col. Alger 'Custer is the ablest man in the Cavalry Corps.' (this for you alone. You may repeat it to our people in Monroe, but not to anyone in Washington.) I thought of you in every battle. Here is something that will please you. I have sworn far less during the late battles than ever before, all owing to the influence of my precious darling. You are in my thoughts always, day and night."

A trace of sweet, haunting fragrance still clung to the withered blossoms. Libbie pressed them to her lips, then folded them carefully inside the letter and tucked both into her bodice. Suddenly she could not bear the four walls of her room any longer. She went out into the garden, walked restlessly along the path, bent to sniff a rosebud, touched the feathery leaves of a sensitive plant to see them close and shrink away. Miss Hyatt's yellow kitten came bouncing over the grass. Libbie picked it up and cuddled it against her cheek.

A step crunched on the path and she turned. Professor Harris was walking slowly toward her, his hands behind his back, his head bent. He looked up, blinked a little, then smiled and bowed. "Ah, Mrs. Custer," he said. "A fine afternoon, is it not?"

"Yes, Professor," she answered. For a moment she hesitated, studying his lined face. There was kindness there, she knew now, and wisdom. Perhaps he could help her with something which had begun to trouble her.

"You have heard from your husband? Forgive me, but I saw the letter in your box and it is unmistakable. I trust that it brought you cheering news?"

"Yes, he is well," she answered. "I wonder if I could talk with you for a moment, sir," she added impulsively.

"Of course, my dear. Let's sit down here on this bench in the shade. Now what is it?"

"It's about something in my husband's letter," she said. "Oh, Professor Harris, he is the kindest, most tender-hearted, most sensitive of men. He appreciates music and poetry more than anyone I have ever known. At the theatre his tears come almost as readily as mine, and when he parted with his mother he could not control his emotion.

"Yet in his letters and in what he tells me of his battles, it almost seems as though—" She paused, then began again. "He has often said that he wishes I could witness some of the charges he heads. The very thought of it turns me sick with horror, yet I cannot tell him that, for he has such wholehearted, boyish pride in his brigade. In one of his letters after Gettysburg he wrote of turning often in his saddle as he charged at the head of his men to look back at the glittering sabres advancing in the sunlight. 'I never expect to see a prettier sight,' he told me. Thinking back on it he said that he could not but exclaim 'Glorious war!'

"Oh, sir, how can it be that the same man who weeps over Little Eva in Uncle Tom's Cabin can see beauty and even take joy in a charge which will bring wounds and death to so many brave men? Is it because I am only a woman that it seems so strange to me and so impossible to understand?"

The Professor listened gravely and when she had finished he waited a moment before he spoke. In the silence the kitten purred loudly under Libbie's stroking hand. "Joy of battle!" the old scholar said at last, shaking his head. "However much we wish the contrary, it is a fact in man's nature, and it has been since the beginning of time. As with the ancient Greeks, even today, some men drink danger like wine and find a strange, wild gaiety in combat which outweighs all its terrors. Alas for the world that it should be so, we can say, but nevertheless it is the fact. There is this other fact to ponder too, Mrs. Custer. The hero Achilles, Homer tells us, was given a choice between a long life of commonplace obscurity and a few brief years made glorious by heroic action and the promise of eternal renown.

"A whole generation of our young men, through no fault of its own, has been fated to fight for us in a dreadful war. They are not given Achilles' choice, but if they were, what then? I think that a few, like your husband, follow a special star and would perhaps make the same choice as that Greek hero did. If they can somehow find beauty and joy in their hard destiny, should we begrudge it to them?"

Libbie stared at him wide-eyed and silent while the meaning of his words sank slowly into her heart and seemed to burn itself there. However much she might wish to deny it, she knew that it was true. Honor, fame, glory, renown, those images were as real and necessary to Autie as his own right hand. Yes, she knew how he would choose.

Suddenly she covered her face with her hands. "Oh, no!" she whispered. It was not a protest but a reply to the Professor's question. "No, I could never begrudge him that, or anything else," she answered.

During the long suspense of that spring campaign, Libbie found some solace in visiting Army hospitals and doing what she could for the wounded. Each visit was an ordeal. Even the best-run of the hospitals was all but unbearable because of the horrible odors, but Libbie could not be dissuaded from going. She was too young to serve at nursing, even if Armstrong had been willing to permit it, for thirty years was the minimum age for the women, but she could bring baskets of fruit and other delicacies, talk to the men and write letters for them. Everywhere her name brought brightened looks of interest, even from the prisoners. "That Custer!" one of the Confederates said. "He takes off his coat, rolls up his sleeves, sets the band to playing. Then, with a shout, the 'Michigan yell,' the whole brigade rushes in."

A letter from Monroe brought news that one of her cousins, Albert Bacon, was dead. "I had thought that everyone outside the Army was safe," she wrote home in sad surprise.

Soon she had something else to occupy her. One of Autie's officers, Jim Christiancy, son of the eminent Judge who was among Custer's most valued friends, was seriously wounded. Libbie arranged for him to be brought from the hospital to her boarding house where she helped to care for him.

Young Christiancy was something of a scapegrace who had cost his father much anxiety and Libbie set about trying to reform him. Her nursing succeeded better than her reforming zeal, however. "He has been without the influence of a good Christian woman," she wrote to her husband. "A good wife would save him from wrong."

About the middle of June, Washington was full of rumors of the Cavalry Corps's new raid, and some of the news was bad. At Trevillian Station two Union divisions were said to be surrounded by the whole Confederate Cavalry and were trying to cut their way out. Editions of papers followed each other thick and fast, each contradicting the last.

"Extra! Extra!" A newsboy came calling along the avenue under Libbie's window. "Read all about it! Extra!"

Suddenly Libbie caught a familiar name in the newsboy's shout and the sound turned her to ice. She could neither move nor speak as the shrill voice came nearer. "Extra! Custer killed! All about Custer being killed!"

Was this how it was to be? Would she have to stand here, helpless and alone, while cold black doom descended upon her forever? Her heart beat in slow, heavy throbs, but still she could not stir.

Someone was coming hurriedly up the stairs. It was not the bounding footfall she longed to hear, but nevertheless it was swift and purposeful. They are coming to tell me, she thought.

Her door stood ajar and now it was pushed open. Autie's friend, Judge Bingham, stood there, concern on his face. Libbie tried to speak, but her stiff lips would not move. She could only look at him, her eyes enormous with her fear.

"Mrs. Custer!" he exclaimed. "I have just come from the War Department. *That rumor is not true*. Armstrong is safe. He was surrounded but he led his men in a great charge and cut through. Once again he has covered himself with glory!"

CHAPTER

8

Armstrong's next letter brought details of the near-disaster. Although most of the brigade managed to fight their way out of the trap, the Confederates captured a number of men and officers, among them the adjutant, Jacob Greene. Johnny Cisco and Eliza also were taken, together with Custer's own headquarters wagon, but they had managed to escape. The wagon had contained Armstrong's extra clothing, bedding, papers and sword-belt. "Everything except my toothbrush, which, as you know, I carry in my pocket. Perhaps now, Libbie, you won't laugh so much at my way of brushing my teeth after every meal," he wrote. "Here's a shopping list for you to replace what I lost."

Worst of all, Libbie's letters to her husband and also her ambrotype were lost to the Rebels. "I regret their loss most of all," he told her. "I don't relish the thought of others amusing themselves by reading what you have written to me. Maybe after this you had better restrain the warmth of what you write to me."

To this hint of censorship Libbie sent a spirited reply.

"What I wrote was holy and sacred. Only cruel people would not understand. There can be nothing low between man and wife if they love each other."

Libbie did not dwell, in her letters to her husband, on what was filling the Washington papers at this time, for fear of worrying him. General Jubal Early, a Confederate cavalry leader, had made a daring raid out of the Shenandoah Valley and was reported to be heading for Washington. The Capital was thrown into a near-panic and troops were massed to defend the city. The ring of forts was strengthened at a feverish pace and President Lincoln himself had been fired upon by advance Rebel skirmishers when he went out to inspect the work.

Before the middle of the month, however, Early had been forced to retire and in the meantime a letter from Autie brought wonderful news. Representative Kellogg had engaged a boat from the Secretary of War in which to bring Senators Chandler and Wilkinson and several ladies from Washington down Chesapeake Bay and up the James River to City Point, and he had suggested that Libbie be one of the party. Even if she could get no closer than Fortress Monroe, Armstrong promised to meet her.

The ride down the sparkling blue bay aboard the President's yacht, River Queen, was a joyful excursion, climaxed for Libbie by a reunion with Autie at City Point. Behind all the gaiety, however, an ominous background of booming siege guns was carried on the breeze from beleaguered Petersburg, bastion of the Confederate capital. Libbie tried to shut her ears to the fateful thunder, for the officers who joined their party were so used to the sound that they no longer noticed it. General Sheridan himself came aboard, summoned his band to play for dancing on the deck and the music soon drowned out the faroff cannon. The men had fought yesterday and perhaps they would fight tomorrow—today they would enjoy the party.

General Sheridan had only learned to dance this summer and he went at it with more vim than art. Though strong and muscular he was very short, and in little Libbie he found the ideal partner. "It was too funny!" she wrote to a friend, describing his vigorous bobbing up and down. Nevertheless she decided that she liked him immensely, especially when he showed his admiration for Armstrong. He, in turn, proceeded to give Libbie full credit for the fact that Custer was one officer whom marriage had not spoiled.

Autie took Libbie back to Washington, but after that she had to endure long, worried, lonely hours again. She spent her time as best she could visiting hospitals, sewing, trimming bonnets for herself and writing letters. Jim Christiancy had recovered enough by now to travel to his home and Professor Harris had left heat-stricken Washington for the duration of the summer. Libbie missed the old scholar's companionship. Her newest solace was in her drawing and painting, and she worked at them daily. "But I can't sit at my easel with hoops on," she confessed to Autie. "If you came today you would find your little wife rather *primitive* in style!"

This was election year, and during the summer the two parties chose their candidates for office. Armstrong believed that soldiers should not be involved in politics and refused to state his preferences. Libbie, of course, could not vote, and found most of the issues confusing. She declared herself "a Lincoln girl," but the Democrats were urging that the War be brought to an end without regard to victory. "Way down in my heart I want peace on any terms, for much as I love my country, I love you more," she confessed, in a letter to Autie. "Why is it that your brigade had to do *everything?*" she inquired, in another. "When people ask your politics I can say truthfully that I don't know, but as for me, I'm still for Abraham!"

There were no official parties or receptions during midsummer, for most of Washington society had left for cooler regions. The President's family had moved from the White House to a spacious cottage on the grounds of the Soldiers' Home, and Lincoln rode or drove to and from his office every day, escorted by a guard of cavalry.

Occasionally Libbie attended the theatre, but on most evenings she either stayed in the boarding house or went with Cara or some other friend to eat ice cream and listen to the Marine Band in the President's Park. Sometimes the long day's heat tempted her to go out alone for a walk in the cool of the evening, but a few experiences with would-be admirers put a stop to that.

"I might as well be in Turkey, for I dare not go out alone without a veil," she wrote indignantly. "In order not to attract attention I dress so plainly that anyone would take me for a dressmaker or a milliner."

To her family in Monroe she wrote her dismay over the lax morals she saw everywhere, even in her own boarding house. "You don't know how barbarous life is here! Family prayers and grace at table are shut out. Even married women flirt outrageously. This city is a Sodom crowded with sin!"

In September the capital was cheered by news that General Sherman had captured the city of Atlanta—a distant victory which seemed of less account to Libbie than the slightest cavalry skirmish in which her Armstrong might take part. Meanwhile the costly and terrible siege of Petersburg dragged on. Without Petersburg Richmond could not be taken and, in spite of the expenditure of countless lives, little progress was apparent.

The high hopes everyone had felt when General Grant took command were ebbing. General Lee was still able to hold him off and a Union victory there still seemed far away.

In contrast with the gloom expressed in the papers, Custer's letters to Libbie were high-spirited and triumphant, filled with accounts of Sheridan's successes in the Shenandoah Valley. He also reported that he had a pet coon which shared his pillow at night and which had made friends with Eliza's goat. These, with a squirrel, captured from a Confederate general, and his own dogs, made up his collection of pets.

In October Libbie decided, with Armstrong's approval, to go for a visit to Mrs. Bacon's relatives in Newark, New Jersey. It was a formidable journey for a young woman alone, even though she had been put in charge of the sleeping-car agent. She spent a wakeful, nervous night in her berth, then was escorted aboard the horse-car in Philadelphia by the polite and solicitous conductor for the five-mile trip across the city to change trains.

The Newark relatives gave her a warm welcome. "They say I have not changed," she wrote to Autie. "They find me very well-preserved in spite of my months of married life!"

On a shopping expedition to New York she was discouraged by the high prices of the silks she had hoped to buy. "I'll wait for spring bargains," she assured her husband thriftily. She contented herself with some lengths of purple material woven of worsted and silk which she bought for thirty-five dollars and also some black alpaca, to be made up for her by a fashionable dressmaker located on Broadway. Gazing into shop windows was fun and the New York ladies looked lovely and stylish to her. "But I think they *embellish* a little," she wrote. "I don't care if fifty Rebels read this letter. I miss your kisses, Autie!" she added boldly.

One morning at the breakfast table in Newark someone brought in a copy of the *New York Times*. It was full of accounts of General Sheridan's ride from Winchester on his black horse, Rienzi, to rally his shaken troops and win the victory at Cedar Creek. "General Custer has arrived in Washington with the captured Rebel flags," someone read aloud.

"Autie in Washington?" Libbie cried. "Oh, I've missed him!" Turning, she stumbled blindly up the stairs to her room where she threw herself brokenheartedly on the bed. It was too cruel that after so many weeks of lonely waiting she should be here, so far away, while Autie was in Washington. The ceremony of presenting the flags to the War Department was set for this very day. Of course he would be gone before she could return.

There was a sudden commotion downstairs. The shrill voices of the children began to reach her. "He's here! He's here! Libbie, he's here!"

Autie it was, bounding up the stairs three at a time to catch her up and kiss away her tears. Because of the illness of Secretary Stanton, the flag presentation was postponed and Custer had come to bring his wife back for the festivities. It was a thrilling return journey; the last forty miles were made in the cab of a locomotive, to save time. On the trip Armstrong told about his brigade's part in the victory of Cedar Creek. "We captured fifty-one cannon in ten days," he told her, his color high, his blue eyes sparkling. "Never since the opening of the War was there such a complete and decisive overthrow of the enemy's cavalry!"

Arrived in the city, Custer hurried to join his men and to ride triumphantly in an omnibus with battle-flags flying from the windows up Pennsylvania Avenue through crowds of cheering onlookers. At the War Department the Secretary accepted the banners, complimented them all, announced that each one would receive a medal and have leave in Washington until the medals were presented and, at the end, made the announcement that Custer had been promoted to Major General.

"*Major General!* I am so proud!" Libbie wrote to her family. "But I must remember your good training and *try* not to be 'stuck up.' "

Election day came and went, and Lincoln was re-elected. The knowledge that the same patient, wise, merciful figure was still to be in the White House inspired the North with new courage. There was a noticeable revival of optimism. "Let's finish the job," men said to one another all across the land.

With his leave over and the front quiet for the time being, Armstrong wrote from Virginia that he was sending for Libbie to visit camp. She would lead a gypsy's life in a tent, he warned her. No comforts, no nice dresses and she must bring her riding habit. Joyfully Libbie traveled by train to Martinsburg where Autie met her. From there they rode in a light spring wagon, with an escort of 150 cavalrymen, forty miles through bright-foliaged autumn country. Perilous country, she learned later, infested by dangerous partisan rangers under Confederate Colonel John Singleton Mosby, who bore a special grudge against Custer.

Tents had been prepared for Libbie's coming in an enclosure of evergreens, one for a bedroom, the other for a reception room, and both were well floored with old barn doors. Eliza beamed at this reunion. "I told you the Ginnel'd be all right, didn't I, Miss Libbie? Nothing can touch Old Curly, the men say, and they're right. Now he's Major Ginnel. 'Custer luck!' Remember, I told you."

"Indeed I do remember," Libbie assured her, with a hug and a kiss.

Within a week after they were settled, they were roused in

the night by news that the Division had orders to withdraw from their position. It was still cold and dark when they breakfasted. Autie had been up for hours with his staff coming and going and messengers arriving and departing at a gallop. Now Libbie sat waiting in the cold blue dawn-light beside the remnants of Eliza's cooking fire, while soldiers packed their tents and her few belongings. Where were they going? Why were they moving so suddenly? Was the enemy near and about to attack? Libbie shivered and drew closer to the glowing ashes. I mustn't bother anyone to ask questions, she told herself. I promised not to complain. Anything is better than to be sent back to Washington alone.

At last her carriage appeared and Armstrong lifted her into it. Then he mounted his big black charger, his staff and color-bearers formed behind him, a trumpet rang out and they set off at a brisk trot. Her soldier-coachman whipped up his horses and followed just behind them while the escort jingled into formation all around the carriage. Libbie was riding with the Army!

The movement proved to be a routine affair, and after another week of camp life, Custer finally established his winter headquarters in an old Virginia mansion at Winchester, Virginia. The owners, Mr. and Mrs. Glass, were charming, cultivated people who made Libbie feel that she was a welcome guest. Eliza was there, too, cooking in the basement and attending cheerfully to all Libbie's wants. Dinners with other officers, parties and dances changed the small, quiet village suddenly into a gay resort. The Michigan Brigade gave a gala ball and each dance on the program was named for a high-ranking "Wolverine."

Besides her carriage, Libbie now had a pretty little saddle horse of her own and Custer presented her with a new side-saddle designed by himself for her special comfort and safety. Whenever his duties allowed, they rode together over the beautiful valley where the Blue Ridge hovered, cloud-like, in the distance. He was plainly delighted with her riding. "You're the prettiest thing I ever saw on a horse, Libbie," he told her. "You took that ditch like a veteran. Next we'll see how you are at fences."

"Fences!" Libbie gasped, glancing with dismay at the high rails dividing the fields.

"There's really nothing to it," he assured her. Suddenly she saw a familiar teasing glint in his eyes. He leaned over and gave her horse a sharp cut with his whip. "Head him straight for the fence, girl. Over you go!" he shouted.

Before she knew what was happening her horse had cleared the rails at a soaring leap and Custer's big black was just behind her. "Oh, that was fun!" she cried, too surprised to be afraid.

"Of course it was. Now that you know how to jump fences we can go farther from camp on our rides. Even if the rebels spot us somewhere we can get away from them," he told her.

"Do you think they are anywhere near, now?" she asked, eying a shadowy clump of woods with misgivings.

"No, but it's always possible," he laughed. "Come, I'll race you back to town."

Tom Custer, now a lieutenant, had joined his brother's staff. In public they maintained a strictly formal relationship, but in their own quarters they were rollicking boys again, noisy and full of hilarious jokes. On their first evening together they began to wrestle. Soon they were tumbling on the floor and rolling over and over while Libbie, helpless with laughter, tried to keep out of range of the flailing arms and legs.

"Wait—let me put Libbie in a safe place," Autie called out, in the midst of the fracas. They separated briefly while he caught her up and swung her to the top of a high chest of drawers and left her there while they resumed the contest. The top of that chest thereafter was the place of detention for Libbie whenever they wanted to tease her. She could not get down and had to stay there until one or the other of them was willing to remove her.

Early in December the weather turned cold and snow fell, filling the valley with hushed whiteness, but there was still work for the cavalry. Armstrong and Tom returned from one of their winter raids brimming with laughter. "There was an old Dutch farmer whose house we wanted to use for head-quarters one night," Tom explained. "He said 'I wouldn't mind for myself, but the Old Lady, she kicks agin it.'" After that, whenever Libbie objected to their antics, Tom quoted the saying, "The Old Lady kicks agin it, Autie. We'll have to stop."

The last weeks of December brought great news for the North. General Sherman had cut his way across the Confederacy from Atlanta to the sea, and Savannah, Georgia, was now in Union hands. Autie had been promised Christmas leave, but it was delayed so that January had arrived before they were able to travel to Michigan. After a brief visit to Monroe they returned to Winchester, bringing Mrs. Bacon and Rebecca Richmond with their party, and the Judge joined them soon after.

Then spring brought preparations for renewed fighting. When her parents departed, Libbie journeyed with them as far as Washington. Once again she must endure loneliness and anxiety, but surely the War could not last much longer. Besides, she had persuaded Rebecca to stay with her for a while in Washington.

Libbie and Rebecca watched the ceremonies of Lincoln's second inaugural from seats in the Senate gallery. Lincoln, they thought, appeared with great dignity but they were too far away to hear his speech clearly. Some words toward the end reached Libbie's ears, however, and they caught at her heart. "With malice toward none, with charity for all, with firmness toward the right as God gives us to see the right—"

Senator Chandler, still Libbie's cavalier, escorted her to the Inaugural Ball where she enjoyed the dancing and was introduced to many celebrities. Most notable was Admiral Farragut, whom she found jolly and unaffected. "The ladies' costumes and jewels were dazzling and the supper-table a miracle of confectionery," she wrote to Autie.

Once again the papers began to carry news of cavalry fighting in Virginia and always Custer's name was prominent in the dispatches. After a final victory over the Confederate General Jubal Early, Custer sent seventeen captured battle flags to Washington. He was too busy to go with them himself, so Libbie was invited to be present at the War Department for the ceremony of their acceptance. She heard her husband praised as wholeheartedly as even she could wish.

She hurried back to her room to resume work on the new battle flag she was making for Autie. It was a handsome affair of red and blue silk edged with white cord, and with crossed sabres stitched in white on both sides. On one of the points Libbie embroidered her own name, and many prayers for her husband's safety went with it when she put it into the care of young Lieutenant Boehm to take to Armstrong.

After a perilous journey through enemy country the banner reached him safely and was first floated in the breeze in the midst of a battle at Five Forks, Virginia. By defeating General Pickett's men there, Sheridan had turned Lee's flank at Petersburg. Within two days the Confederate leader had to abandon the city and was in full retirement westward. The Confederate government thereupon fled from their capital. Richmond had fallen at last!

There was no time for the cavalry to savor their triumph. Lee was on the loose, and if he could reach Lynchburg he would find enough supplies waiting for him to launch a new campaign. Sheridan's cavalry must catch and halt him—but where? After a week of headlong riding in search of Lee's elusive, swiftly moving columns, Custer finally found him, on April 8, near the little town of Appomattox Station, Virginia.

Custer knew well that he could not hold even what was left of the Army of Northern Virginia without infantry support, and the infantry was far behind. But he must try. He dismounted most of his troopers and stationed them across the road. There was a night of savage, desperate fighting in the darkness, and soon another division of Union cavalry arrived to relieve him. Even so, unless the infantry came up the two leaders knew that they could not hold back the enemy.

Custer himself galloped to Sheridan's headquarters and told him the situation. "Lee must be held *at any cost!*" Sheridan stated grimly.

The morning of April 9 dawned cold and foggy. Through the mist Custer could see enemy batteries swinging into line and infantry preparing for an assault along the road. Cavalry could never stand against so massive an attack. "We'll charge on their flank as they advance. That will slow them down, at least," he decided, and ordered his troopers into a column of squadrons.

All at once he heard the sound of wild, hoarse cheering. There, on his left, the pine wood was blue with uniforms. The Union infantry had arrived and it was aligned across the road in solid strength.

On the other side of the valley the gray-clad troops seemed to hesitate. They too had sighted the blue mass. Suddenly out of their midst a single horseman came riding. Above him fluttered something white. It was a towel tied to a stick—a flag of truce—*of surrender!*

An aide, sitting his mount beside Custer gave a low exclamation. "Wherever could they have found a towel, and one so white?" he marveled aloud. After only a moment of hesitation Custer touched his horse's sides with his spurs and galloped forward to receive the white flag and all that it implied.

CHAPTER

9

At news of the fall of Richmond all Washington had gone wild. The shrill, exultant shouts of newsboys filled the streets and, like everyone else, Libbie rushed out to purchase a paper and read the glorious words. Meanwhile the air was shaken by a salute from eight hundred guns, three hundred for Petersburg and five hundred for Richmond. Church bells clanged, bands went marching along the avenues, children poured out of school and clerks and workmen from offices and factories. All waved flags, singing and shouting their joy. Everyone who had a carriage or wagon draped it with bunting and entered one of the spontaneous parades, together with suddenly activated regiments of foot and cavalry and hordes of civilian riders. Even fire departments sent their engines galloping through the streets letting off blasts of steam.

On Tuesday evening the city was illuminated in honor of the victory. The Capitol glowed with light from dome to basement, and a great transparency, lit by jets of gas, covered the western pediment. "This is the Lord's doing: It is marvellous in our eyes," the sign read. All the other government buildings were illuminated too, even the prisons and insane asylums. Business blocks, hotels, private residences, all put some sort of lights in their windows, if only tallow candles, and everywhere there were flags and bunting.

A crowd gathered at the White House hoping for a glimpse of the President, but word came that he was already in Richmond. It was said that Lee had fled safely from Petersburg but that the Union troops were close behind him, Sheridan's cavalry leading the pursuit. *Sheridan's cavalry!* Libbie read, her heart turning over within her. Then of course Autie is there at the very spearpoint of the advance. He's still in danger!

On Wednesday, Secretary of State Seward was riding in his carriage through the jubilant streets when his horses became frightened and overturned the carriage. The Secretary was painfully injured and the news brought President Lincoln back from Richmond. Those who saw him arrive on the River Queen said that Lincoln's face had lost its look of gaunt fatigue and was luminous, almost beautiful. His long and terrible ordeal was near its end at last.

Before dawn on April 10 Libbie was awakened by booming cannon. It could mean only one thing, but still she must know. She flung a wrapper over her nightgown and ran downstairs. Yes, newsboys were already out in the rain-filled darkness and their cries came clearly. "Lee surrenders! Read about Grant's great victory! Lee surrenders!"

The other boarders were also in the halls in all sorts of disarray, but no one noticed or commented on anyone's clothing. Heedless of the rain, Libbie ran into the street barefooted and bought a paper from the first shouting boy. Tears of happiness blurred the print, but surely this was the end of the War. The end of fighting, of killing, of danger for her own dear love! Surely, surely. The headlines said that it was General Custer who had received the first white flag, but until she heard from him or saw him with her own eyes she could not be certain that he was truly safe.

Suddenly she remembered what excitement had wiped from her mind. The Committee on the Conduct of the War and their wives were to leave Washington and travel by gunboat to Richmond. Senator Chandler, a member of the Committee, had invited Libbie to go along. Perhaps word of her coming could be sent to Autie and he would find some way to meet her? Her heart began to beat so fast that she was breathless when she reached her room. Hurriedly she dressed and packed her small valise.

Once again Libbie traveled down the great bay, this time on the President's gunboat, the *Baltimore*. Sunshine was lacking but no weather could dampen the happiness of those aboard, nor could the fact that a pilot had to be taken on to guide them safely through the torpedoes.

Admiral Porter came aboard at City Point and Libbie found him pleasant but not so natural and unassuming as Farragut. At her plea he sent a telegram to Custer in care of General Grant's headquarters. "Mrs. Custer will be in Richmond to-morrow."

At first view of the grim, fire-blackened ruins of Richmond a hush fell over the gay group aboard the vessel. All the fires had been quenched and the streets leading up from the dock cleared of debris, but an acrid smell of smoke lingered and stung their nostrils as they walked. The few white people whom they passed stared at them with blank, dazed faces, but the Negroes greeted them with laughter and welcoming cheers. To them it seemed that the promised "year of jubilee" had indeed arrived.

General Weitzel had set up his headquarters in the home of Jefferson Davis, the high, square, pillared mansion which had served as the Confederate White House. When he and Mrs. Weitzel learned that Custer had been notified of his wife's arrival, he invited Libbie to stay with them and to remain as their guest after the rest of the party returned to Washington.

Libbie therefore found herself sleeping that night in Jefferson Davis's bed and the next in Mrs. Davis's. Never in my wildest dreams could I have imagined such a thing possible! she thought as she lay, too excited to sleep, staring at the high, white ceiling. Even now it was difficult to believe.

The next day she spent admiring the handsome furnishings— grand piano, mirrors, draperies, Sèvres china—and making friends with a small, lonely black-and-tan dog which, the house-keeper told her, had belonged to the Davis's little son who had died.

On the second morning of her stay Libbie was awakened by a familiar swift step on the stairs. "Autie!" she cried, sitting up in the great bed and holding out her arms to him as he burst into the room. After the first blissful moment she drew back to look at him again. "How thin you are, my darling!" she cried, appalled.

His eyes seemed to look at her out of deep shadows and there were lines and hollows in his cheeks she had never seen before. Then his smile flashed as bright as ever and suddenly he was her gay-hearted boy again. "I'm wondering if I can ever live down the fact that you reached Richmond before me!" he said. "Here I've been fighting for four long years to get here and now that I've made it, what do I find but my little Libbie already in possession!"

There was so much to tell and to talk over and to plan for. "How will you like to be just a captain's wife?" he asked her suddenly, his face sober. "You know my rank of Major-General of Volunteers is only temporary. In the Regular Army I'm still only a captain."

He was looking at her anxiously. Was he troubled about such a thing at *this* time? "Autie, Autie, it's *you* I love and want, not rank or honors or glory, nothing in all the world but *you!*" She threw herself into his arms again, almost weeping.

Soon he was bringing out of his pockets treasures to show her. The first was the fringed towel which had been the surrender flag on the fateful morning at Appomattox and the other was a letter addressed to her in a strange hand.

She turned it over wonderingly. "For me?" she asked.

"Read it, Libbie," he said, his blue eyes sparkling.

"My dear Madam," she read aloud. "I respectfully present to you the small writing table on which the conditions for the surrender of the Confederate Army of Northern Virginia were written by General Grant—and permit me to say, Madam, that there is scarcely an individual in our service who has contributed more to bring this about than your very gallant husband.

Yours very respectfully
Phil. H. Sheridan
Major General"

Libbie read the letter over again in happy amazement. "Oh, what a priceless honor!" she whispered. "We'll treasure it forever, won't we, Autie? What a tribute to you, but no more than you deserve. Tell me how it all happened."

"The meeting between Grant and Lee was held at Appomattox Court House in a brick residence belonging to a Mr. McLean," Custer told her. "I was there, waiting outside with other officers while the two leaders conferred. After it was over and the commanding generals had ridden away, all those of us who were left swarmed into the room where the surrender took place, anxious to get souvenirs. Sheridan had first choice be-

cause of his rank, of course, and he set an example by paying
Mr. McLean twenty dollars in gold for the little pine table they
had used to sign the documents on. He told me that he had
kept those two ten-dollar gold pieces on his person all during
the war in case he should be taken prisoner. I was certainly
the most astonished man in the world when he gave the table
to me to take to you."

"What did you do with the table, Autie?" Libbie asked. "Is
Mr. McLean going to ship it to me?"

"Ship it?" he shook his head. "There'd be little chance of its
ever reaching you. No, I carried it away myself. It's at my
headquarters now, safely under guard."

"But Autie?" she asked, puzzled. "However could you carry
a table away on horseback?"

"Why, I balanced it on my head," he answered, chuckling
and kissing her again. "Now get up and pack your things.
You're coming back to camp with me. You'll be riding north
with the Army, Libbie. Will you like to be gipsying again,
sweetheart?"

"I'll love it!" Libbie answered truthfully.

They returned to camp together, traveling part of the way
on the Southside Railroad. "You're the first woman to ride this
line since the capture of Richmond," Autie told her.

At Armstrong's headquarters Libbie was welcomed once
again by Tom, Eliza, Johnny Cisco, the staff officers and hordes
of grinning, jubilant troopers. A new saddle horse was waiting
for her too, a beautiful pacer named Custis Lee. Autie himself
had a fine new mount, a spirited bay stallion called Don Juan.
Both animals had been captured from the Confederates and then
bought for his own use by Custer.

They breakfasted in camp on the morning of April fifteenth.
It had rained during the night and there were still clouds in the

sky, but the air was balmy. The scent of new grass and spring flowers mingled with the stronger odors of woodsmoke, coffee and bacon from the cooking-fires. Eliza had just finished serving them when an aide came hurrying up to the General's tent. His face was pale under his tan and he broke unceremoniously into their conversation without waiting to be questioned. "I'm bringing bad news, General, the worst I ever carried. President Lincoln is dead. He was shot last night at Ford's Theatre by an actor named John Wilkes Booth. He died early this morning."

Libbie gave a choked gasp and clutched at the edge of the table for support as though struck by a stunning physical blow. That kind, strong face, as clear before her now as though it were imprinted on her eyelids! Dimly she felt Autie lift her as she fell and carry her to the bed in their tent, then heard him hurry away. Eliza began to wail somewhere nearby. All about her the camp filled with sounds as the news spread. Men's voices, first low and incredulous, then loud and angry; booted feet hurrying to and fro; horses' hoofbeats; the jingle of mounting and dismounting riders; trumpet-calls that echoed each other farther and farther into the distance; beneath it all a hushed, deep, mournful murmur like surf on an ocean shore.

The next day was Easter Sunday. The chaplain held a service and, without urging on anyone's part, it was attended by every man who was not on duty. When the chaplain tried to speak of Lincoln, however, his voice failed him and he could not continue and many of the troopers wept unashamedly.

They remained in camp for two days more. When they set out for Petersburg, Libbie, mounted on her new pacer, rode with Autie at the head of his troops. Custis Lee was a perfect riding horse, spirited, yet gentle and smooth-gaited. The weather was clear and warm and bright after the rain, and surely no countryside was ever more beautiful than these green valleys and wooded hills of Virginia. Many fruit-trees were still in full bloom, lilacs and honeysuckle sent out their fragrance from fence and dooryard and level drifts of white dogwood shone through the shadows of the woods.

Even with peace and victory hovering like living presences above them the men rode soberly and quietly. It was all too new, too strange after four long years. Added to that strangeness was the Union's loss, which everyone felt to be his own.

From Petersburg Libbie went back to Washington to gather up her clothing and make arrangements to return to the army. "After this we must never be separated again," she told Armstrong earnestly as she said goodbye.

Washington, which she had left so happy and exultant, was draped in mourning. Gloom, suspicion, and demands for revenge filled the newspapers. Mobs gathered on the slightest pretext and orators denounced all Confederates alike. It seemed impossible to believe that Booth had acted alone or that he was not a part of a vast, far-reaching Rebel conspiracy. Libbie remained in the city only long enough to ship the precious little pine table to her father in Monroe and to pack the things she would be needing. It was a relief to get away and back to camp again.

There she learned some dismaying news. General Sheridan had received orders to go at once to New Orleans. Grant had decided that the South should be held under military control for a time, and there was danger also from the French and Austrians, who had set up an empire across the border in Mexico. Sheridan had asked especially that his two favorites, Generals Merritt and Custer, be sent with him for that duty.

"General Sheridan is leaving directly and I'll have to join him right after the Grand Review in Washington," Autie told her. "I shan't be able to go back to Monroe with you after all, darling. I have to obey orders, even though it means another parting."

But Libbie shook her head. "No!" she answered. Her chin was high and her cheeks scarlet. "No, Autie, I said that we would never be separated again, and we shan't, if I can help it! I'm going with you. You've said yourself that I never make any trouble, and so has General Sheridan. I'm going with you."

May 23, the first day of the two-day Grand Review of the Union Armies, dawned bright and clear after a rain-washed night. Custer's men had been camped at nearby Bladensburg and they had spent their time polishing boots, brass, and saddle-leather and grooming their mounts until they shone like satin. Washington was filled with visitors, among them Emmanuel Custer who had come to watch his two sons take part in the triumphant spectacle. The city had put off its draperies of mourning and once again it was bright with flowers and flags that fluttered in the brisk wind.

The crowds had begun to gather early. Hours before the parade was scheduled to start the sidewalks were thronged and every window along the route was packed with faces. Libbie and Armstrong's father had been given good seats from which to watch, only a short distance from the stand in front of the White House where President Andrew Johnson and General Grant stood waiting to receive the salutes of the Army.

At nine o'clock a single cannon boomed out the signal that the great review had begun. This was the day of Washington's own Army of the Potomac; tomorrow Sherman and his Army of the Tennessee would pass. Leading his troops in the place of honor rode the serious, bearded figure of General Meade riding a flower-garlanded horse, with his flag-bearers and gold-braided staff just behind him. After him came more bright flags, then a band pumping out music as it strode along while its polished instruments flashed and glittered in the sun. The crowds cheered, the bands played, the beautifully groomed horses curvetted and danced. Little boys shrieked their joy from branches of trees all along the way while ladies waved their handkerchiefs in a white snowstorm of tribute.

Now the first horsemen of the Cavalry Corps clattered into view. There were a few murmurs of disappointment at Sheridan's absence, but the crowds cheered loyally for General Wesley Merritt, the senior division commander, who rode in Sheridan's place. Merritt's division with its bands and tossing banners passed and then suddenly the crowd's cheering swelled into a wilder roar as the people caught sight of the fluttering red neckerchiefs that decked the next division's troopers. "Custer! Custer!" they yelled.

The lithe young horseman riding just ahead of his flag-bearers glanced about under the wide, rakish brim of his hat. The throngs could see his long yellow curls, the blueness of his eyes and the gleam of his white teeth as he smiled and saluted with his drawn sabre. So this was the fabulous Custer, the daredevil leader whose exploits had filled the newspapers for so long—"The Boy General with the Golden Locks."

"What a superb, mettlesome horse and look how he can ride him!" . . . "He's never lost a flag or failed to capture a cannon he went after!" . . . "Hurrah for Old Curly!" . . . "Custer, the Murat of the American Army." . . . "Let's give him three cheers. Custer! Custer! Custer!" The shouts grew louder and more deafening as the long river of blue flowed up the avenue.

At the Treasury building where the avenue curved, a chorus of three hundred young girls in white dresses sat waiting. As Custer appeared they rose to their feet and began to sing and to toss flowers out upon the passing troopers. Custer leaned to catch one of the bouquets and in that instant Don Juan caught the bit between his teeth and bolted.

Libbie had been watching Merritt's division pass and was growing more and more excited as the cheers for Custer came ringing up the avenue. "He'll be next, Father Custer!" she cried, clutching at the old man's sleeve. "Listen! They're cheering for him now."

All at once the sound of the cheering hushed strangely and the next moment a single horseman appeared in the distance coming on at breakneck speed. "Why, it looks like Autie!" Libbie cried.

Everyone in the grandstand had risen in alarm as the rider came rocketing past them, bare-headed, his yellow hair bright in the sun. "It *is* Autie! Don Juan has run away with him. Oh, I can't bear to look!" and she covered her face with her hands.

"Don't worry, Libbie! He's got the horse under control now," Emmanuel Custer reassured her. "There never was a horse Autie couldn't manage. He's turned him now, and he's riding back. Well, there's something I'll never let the boy hear the last of. Run away with at a parade!"

The spectators around them were beginning to settle back into their seats. "Well, there's Custer for you," a voice said acidly just beyond Libbie. "Anything to show off. A grandstand play if ever there was one."

"Don't you believe that his horse really got away from him?" another voice asked, while Libbie listened, amazed and indignant. "I'd bet my life he didn't," the first speaker answered. "There isn't a better horseman in our army. Just another bid for attention and glory, like so many of his others. And all the papers will play it up, of course. There'll probably be pictures, too."

Libbie wanted to jump to her feet, confront the speaker and

denounce him then and there for falsehood and libel against
her husband, who had proved himself on so many battlefields.
Instead she sat frozen and motionless, too angry to move. At
least Father Custer hadn't heard what was said, that was one
comfort. After a while she was able to lean forward enough
to see the speakers. Both were officers and one of the faces
looked a little familiar to her. I've seen him somewhere, she
thought. Yes, I remember now. He was with General Pleasanton last year. How could he say such a spiteful, wrong thing?
Of course it's only jealousy. Tears stung her eyes, but she
blinked them back resolutely. Even if Autie *had* done it on
purpose—and she would never admit that he had—it would not
have been for the reason that man gave, but out of boyish high
spirits, nothing more!

Now the people were cheering again. "Custer! Custer!" they
were calling. There he came, Don Juan controlled and submis-
sive under him, riding past as only he could ride with his flag-
carriers and his gold-braided staff officers, his trumpeters and
his mounted band and the long lines of troopers clattering
jauntily behind him. "Custer! Custer! Custer!"

CHAPTER

10

Directly after the Grand Review, Custer, with Libbie beside him, rode back to the Third Division's encampment. He would now have to say goodbye to the men who had followed him so loyally for so long. She waited with the officers of his staff on a little rise of ground and watched him ride down the long lines, waving his hat to them for the last time in the familiar, gallant gesture. The troopers began to cheer as he passed, the roar swelled, grew louder, wilder, more frenzied. A storm of blue caps flew into the air, and some men even broke ranks and pushed forward to clasp their young leader's hand. Libbie could see the gleam of tears on many sunburnt faces. At the end, to her surprise, came a sudden great cheer for "Mrs. Custer!"

"Ride forward, Libbie, and acknowledge it," Tom urged her. She lifted Custis Lee's rein, the horse started up, but suddenly she checked him again. "Oh Tom, no! I can't bear it!" she whispered, her voice choking. "It's sweet of them, but they mustn't see me crying so foolishly. It's all for Autie, anyway."

During the long ride back to the city through the late sunlight, Armstrong was silent. What is going through his mind, Libbie wondered. Four long years—four long *lifetimes* of struggle and hardship and danger and triumph and glory! They are all behind him now, and still—still he's *only twenty-five years old!*

All at once the voice of the old Greek scholar was in her ears, as he had spoken to her in Miss Hyatt's garden of Achilles and his hard choice. Libbie's heart gave a great, exultant leap. The War is over and Autie is safe. He has all the renown and glory that any man could wish and surely, *surely* a long lifetime stretches before him, now that peace is here. He has been granted *both!* She bent her head and breathed a small, silent prayer of thanksgiving.

That evening, after a hasty gathering of luggage and arrangements for shipping their horses, they boarded the train which was to carry them toward their new assignment in the South. Eliza was there too, and Tom and the officers of Custer's staff. Besides their own party the whole train was crowded with a joyful, jubilant throng of discharged men traveling at long last to their homes.

It was true that many bore sad scars of war, empty sleeves, crutches and some even had to be lifted down from the car on stretchers. But they were returning home, and at even the smallest station, people and flags and bands and eager, loving faces waited to welcome the heroes.

We would have received just such a welcome back to our home, Libbie thought with a wistful sigh, and for a moment pictures of the green-painted Monroe railway station, the lake, the familiar tree-shaded streets and the faces of her parents were vivid in her mind. Resolutely she pushed them out of her thoughts. I'm where I want most of all in the world to be, here beside Autie, wherever he's bound.

By this time Libbie had learned that they were not to stay in New Orleans, as she had first understood. Sheridan was giving Custer command of one of his two cavalry divisions. His orders were to march from the Red River in Louisiana to Houston, Texas, with a two-fold purpose. One was to restore and maintain order in that still-turbulent state, while the other was to make a show of force along the Mexican border.

During the time that the United States had been occupied with its Civil War, the French Emperor, Napoleon III, had sent an army and set up a puppet ruler in Mexico. Intrigues dangerous to the safety of the United States were known to be in progress between unsubdued Confederate officers and troops and the Archduke Maximilian, the so-called Emperor of Mexico.

Libbie had hunted up a map and found the location of Houston. To her it seemed as remote as the polar regions. However, as she wrote to her family, "I am indifferent to the points of the compass so long as I am not left behind."

There was no dining car aboard the train, so at one of the stops in Ohio they hurried into the station dining room. A single long table was set up for the passengers. To Eliza's dismay the General steered her, along with Libbie, to the table and seated her between himself and his wife.

The proprietor was quick to protest. "That girl will have to leave. I don't serve colored folks," he stated, scowling.

"You haven't provided any other tables, and she must eat," the General told him, with a disarming smile.

"She can go hungry for all I care," the man said, still standing threateningly behind her. "She'll have to get out."

Panic-stricken, poor Eliza tried to rise, but Custer restrained her. He looked the man up and down with eyes that were suddenly icy in their blueness, then reached for a serving platter, filled Eliza's plate, Libbie's and his own, and began to eat. His staff followed his example and, what was more, gave the man such defiant glances that at last he went sulkily back to his place.

Eliza was so frightened that she could eat very little before the train's whistle warned them that they would have to leave. "Take some of that bread and butter and make a sandwich for Eliza, Libbie," Custer directed. He himself gathered up a whole large pie, and marched out of the dining room, as erect as though on parade, carrying it balanced on his palm under the nose of the infuriated proprietor. The loafers on the station platform did not soon forget the sight of a major general in uniform carrying such a burden!

They traveled by rail as far as Louisville, then boarded a river steamer for the rest of the journey. The "Ruth," as the vessel was named, would carry them down the Ohio into the Mississippi and then, by that great river, to New Orleans. Libbie had heard of the beauty and luxury of these towering paddle-wheelers, but it amazed her none the less. The cabins were spacious and comfortable, the lounges and dining saloon paneled in polished wood. A large painting of the Biblical Ruth adorned the wall of the main cabin, while other figures of her carrying her sheaves decorated the glass of the stateroom doors and the elaborate metal chandeliers.

The meals, served by processions of white-coated waiters, were as elaborate and sumptuous as in the finest hotels. An orchestra furnished music to the diners. On the decks there were comfortable chairs from which the passengers could watch the passing shores and the other vessels that plied the waters, first of the Ohio, then of the Mississippi.

Libbie was impressed by the high levees along the second

river. How strange to be looking over the embankment and down upon land lower than the water upon which their vessel rode! The steamer had to make frequent stops to take on wood to feed the ravenous fires of the boilers. When a stop was made at night, knots of resinous wood, burning in iron baskets, hung over the vessels sides to light the work. The flaring glare and inky shadows gave a dramatic quality to the scene of hurrying, dark figures reflected in black water. Like some weird and sinister painting of the nether world, Libbie thought.

Custer and his staff were too active and restless to stay for long in the lounges or the deck chairs. They roamed the vessel over, watched the engines and learned their workings, made friends with the captain and the pilot and were always the first ashore when they tied up on the bank of a new state.

"Come along, Old Lady!" Tom would call out to Libbie. "Don't you want to set your feet on the soil of Tennessee?"— Or Arkansas or Mississippi, as the case might be.

Soon the seemingly inapproachable pilot invited Libbie into the high, round tower of his wheelhouse. She sat there with her sewing for many hours during the journey, listening to his tales of adventure along the river in time of storm, flood, fire or explosion, while he pointed out memorable landmarks along the shore.

Sometimes they passed over shoal water, traveling slowly and gingerly, while a sailor in the bow made soundings with a plumb line to learn the river's depth. At regular intervals his droning voice called out "Mark twain!" while the pilot steered them with infinite caution along their course.

Sometimes, in spite of all the pilot's care, the ship would run aground on a newly formed sand-bar with a great groaning of timbers and creak of machinery. If all other efforts failed and the engines merely ploughed the vessel deeper into the sand, the two spars attached to the forward deck were swung out. By the aid of rope and tackle and these "stilts," the flat-bottomed craft was dragged over the bar and into deeper waters again.

In the evenings after dinner the Custer party sat on the deck enjoying the balmy summer air. One of the aides had brought his guitar and they filled the nights with songs of every kind from the popular sentimental ballads, "Lorena" and "Aura Lee," to rough, hilarious camp ditties and, at Libbie's special request, old hymn tunes.

At one of the stops a tall, fair man came swinging up the gangplank on crutches. Hearing his name, Custer hastened to greet him and to introduce himself. They grasped each other's hands and soon Armstrong brought the Confederate General Hood to meet Libbie. He was traveling only to the next city on the river, but in that brief time the two men found so much to talk about that they parted with regret.

As they journeyed farther south the vegetation changed, and grew more luxuriant. Soon they were passing avenues of palmettos, groves of orange trees with their golden fruit and waxy-white, fragrant blossoms mingled with their dark leaves, and blossoming, spicy-scented oleanders. The plantations now looked more prosperous and the mansions larger. Galleries encircled the upper stories of the houses and the travelers often glimpsed families dining in comfort there, shaded by blinds of matting.

When they finally left the steamer at New Orleans, Libbie looked back at the tall white vessel with a regretful sigh. What a magically carefree interlude life aboard her had been! She would never forget it.

New Orleans, too, held a special magic, she soon discovered. Charming old streets, fine restaurants, enchanting markets and shops where the clerks waited on them with unhurried French courtesy—everything delighted her. Custer pronounced the coffee the best he had ever tasted and drank so many cups of it that even the creole who served them exclaimed "Mon Dieu!" in dismay.

General Sheridan entertained them in the beautiful mansion he had leased for his headquarters. They also called upon the aged and ailing General Winfield Scott, whose picture, mounted on a rearing steed, had decorated the Bacon parlor. Seeing the old hero of the Mexican War now so infirm saddened Libbie, but she was all the more touched by the lavish praise he heaped on Custer's war record.

Their stay in New Orleans was brief and soon they boarded another steamer for their trip up the Red River. This vessel was far smaller and less luxurious than the "Ruth," and the river itself was unattractive. A recent flood had left the trees along the banks caked with mud halfway up their trunks, and their branches were raggedly festooned with dismal gray moss. Narrow in some places, wide in others, the stream was so full of obstructions that it seemed miraculous for the pilot to find a channel.

With whistle screeching at every turn, sometimes rushing forward at full steam, sometimes backing hastily away with a great shuddering of engines, bumping against the muddy banks, scraping over shags and shoals, the vessel made its slow progress. On the sand-bars and along the soft red clay banks for which the river was named, innumerable alligators lay basking in the sun, and sand-hill cranes stood on one foot in the shallow water. "I don't blame them for not wanting to put the other foot down into that slimy mess!" Libbie exclaimed.

Custer tried his skill with a rifle on the alligators and soon learned how hard their hides were. Unless he hit them on the vulnerable spot just behind the eye his bullets were useless. He practiced doggedly and before the trip was over he had accounted for many of the creatures.

Youth and high spirits and the efforts of the friendly and jovial captain kept their party cheerful in spite of the desolate landscape through which they traveled. They laughed, played jokes on each other, and filled each evening with song, just as before.

They arrived at Alexandria, Louisiana, where the Division was to be assembled, toward the latter part of June. As they stepped ashore a tall man came forward, lifting his hat to Libbie. She looked at him, sensing something familiar in his face, then gave a little cry of recognition. It was the Southern boy who had gone to school in Monroe, the romantic, dark-eyed beau who had left all the girls sighing when he returned to his Southern home just before the War! He was sadly changed, Libbie noted with quick compassion. She introduced him to her husband and they had some moments of happy reminiscence.

The house assigned to the Custers was large and airy and had a well-stocked library, but it lacked every modern convenience of the time. For washing, the muddy river water had to serve, while the only supply for drinking came from a huge cistern where rainwater from the roof had been collected during the rainy season, now long past. Even when the pollywogs, wigglers and other matter had been strained out of it, the Custers learned that it was wise to let a glassful stand untouched until the sediment had settled to the bottom, before drinking it.

The former owners, accustomed to retinues of servants, had made no effort to install comforts that any Michigan mechanic would have thought essential. There was no cellar, for the house stood on high posts imbedded in the spongy ground. Pigs, chickens, dogs and cats, even cattle roamed at will under the house, and it was difficult to convince Eliza that alligators did not, also. As summer advanced, the humid heat in the daytime was overpowering, and as soon as the sun began to sink, mosquitoes swarmed up from the stagnant bayous.

Eliza did her best to defeat them by burning raw cotton in kettles in the rooms, but the smudge of smoke was almost worse than the insects. The bed, draped in mosquito netting, offered the only real refuge, and Libbie learned to spend her afternoons enthroned there with her sewing, reading or writing letters, protected by the netting.

In the evenings after the heat of the day, Armstrong, Libbie, and the aides mounted their horses and rode through the lush and verdant valley. They often went for miles along country roads hedged high on either side by osage oranges and dew-laden white roses whose mingled fragrance filled the cooling air. Mockingbirds, glad of relief from the heat, sang in every bush and, on moonlit nights, continued their music until dawn.

Sometimes the General and his aides went alligator hunting and sometimes fishing in the bayous. Libbie was always invited to go along and she always went, although the alligators terrified her and she had little taste for fishing. The black, sluggish water of the twisting bayous upon which their little boat floated, the tangled vegetation on the shores, the dank odors and the weird shapes of the gnarled tree-trunks that rose from the muddy banks gave a strange, nightmarish quality to the scene. Like the setting of a sensational murder tale, Libbie thought with a shudder. Nevertheless to be here, or anywhere with Autie, was far better than to be left behind.

Custer had found many problems waiting for him in Alexandria. The end of the War had brought only an uneasy peace to the countryside, where the returned Confederate soldiers, the newly organized civil authorities, and the hordes of freed slaves were all engaged in bitter conflict. Lawlessness, violence, robbery, and even murder were commonplace. Most of the citizens, in spite of their Confederate sympathies, declared themselves relieved that the Army had arrived and would bring some semblance of law and order.

Maintaining order among the civilian population was not Custer's hardest task, however. His own soldiers had been gathered from all over the West to form this new division. They were mostly volunteers whose periods of enlistment had only a short time more to run. Now that the War was over they were resentful at being kept in uniform after many of their comrades had returned to their homes. Most of them had been doing only garrison duty before and had never seen combat, hence had not experienced the discipline it would have given them. They were restless, surly, and insubordinate. Gangs of them went raiding and pillaging about the countryside in defiance of all orders.

Their officers had lost control and were being bullied by their own men. One night a colonel was shot at in his tent. Later a ruffianly trooper, who had boasted of robberies and crimes and of several previous desertions during the War, deserted once again. Finally a hitherto good soldier, a much-respected sergeant, refused to obey an order given by a superior officer and led a mutiny against him.

The two culprits were arrested and court-martialed. When they were found guilty and sentenced to death, a furious protest swept through the division. A petition was circulated in behalf of the well-liked sergeant, signed even by the officer against whom he had rebelled. It might have had an effect upon Custer, the commanding officer, if, at the same time, he had

not received a series of anonymous threats that before the
sentence was carried out he himself would be shot down by
the man's regiment.

Armstrong had tried to keep the news of the coming execu-
tions and of the threats against his own life from Libbie, but
it reached her ears. He refused all her pleas and those of his
staff to wear side-arms when he attended the grim ceremony,
and in an agony of helpless terror Libbie watched him mount
and ride away unarmed to the place of execution. She listened
until the last echo of his horse's hoof-beats had died away, then
flung herself on her bed and covered her head with a pillow.
At least I can shut out the sound of those dreadful volleys, she
thought. And of the other shots that may come too!

The five thousand troops of the Division were assembled to
form a hollow square, the prisoners were led out and blindfolded, the firing squad stood ready. Then Custer himself, with
a set, expressionless face, rode out and slowly made the circuit
of the troops, passing so close to the threatening regiment that
the front ranks could have reached out and touched him as he
went by. When he had finished he reined in his horse and gave
a signal to his provost marshal. The aide quietly stepped forward, took the blindfolded sergeant by the arm, and led him
out of range of the bullets just before the deserter was shot
down.

The sergeant had been spared and given a chance to redeem
himself, while military discipline had been maintained and the
commanding officer had shown that he would not be in-
timidated.

By August the Division was ready to begin its long march
into Texas. An ambulance had been fitted up as a traveling
wagon and to serve as a bedroom for Libbie and the General.
Her valise and shawl and a box for lunch were strapped to the

side, accessible but out of the way. There were pockets for her needlework and books, and one of the soldiers had fitted a cover on a canteen and stitched "Lady Custer" upon it in cavalry-yellow silk.

They left the Red River Valley and climbed onto a table-land covered with pine forests. The tall trees were sparse and scraggy. Although they afforded a little shade during the day they also seemed to shut off any breeze, and the air under them was stifling. Libbie had looked forward to sleeping in a tent again as she had done with such enjoyment in Virginia, but mere mention of the numbers of rattlesnakes in the region changed her mind. By sleeping in the wagon she avoided the rattlesnakes, but there was plenty of other wildlife—lizards, horned toads, centipedes, scorpions and tarantulas, to say nothing of ticks and chiggers and mosquitoes. The wagon-bed was hard, and Libbie, in far more fear of being sent home than of any creeping or crawling creature, did not complain to anyone but Eliza. That sympathetic ally tried to help matters by stuffing a pillow for her with moss from the pine trees. When a horned toad was found inside the moss that night Eliza tried hay, with the result that Libbie was awakened in the darkness by one of the wagon-mules trying to devour her pillow.

Blistered by the sun, drenched with dew and rain, bitten by insects, prostrated for days by a bout of "break-bone" fever, Libbie nevertheless proved herself the best of troopers. Reveille came long before dawn and she learned to bathe and dress by the light of a single tallow candle in seven minutes, flat. During the day's march she stubbornly endured hunger and cold, thirst and heat rather than ask for any special rests or favors other than the regular halts the column observed.

There were many terrifying moments, such as when it was

necessary to cross one of the high-banked Texas rivers on a pontoon bridge. Sometimes Libbie made the traverse in the wagon: the four mules seemed to sit down and slide their way to the water's edge while the driver kept his foot on the brake, shouting oaths and holding them back as best he could. Then came the crossing on the swaying, bouncing bridge itself and after that the climb up a steep bank again. Crossing on horseback was equally frightening, for her spirited, nervous mount never seemed to get used to this particular ordeal.

In the evenings after the long march, however, when they sat around the campfire and sang the old songs, came hours which seemed to Libbie to make up for all the day's endurances. Weary in body but blissful in spirit she was lifted at last by Autie into the wagon-bedroom. Often too tired to finish her nightly prayers before she fell asleep, Libbie was able to reassure herself by thinking "My prayers are very short, for I really have nothing to ask, since the best of everything on earth has already been given to me."

CHAPTER

11

When they reached Hempstead, Texas, the Division went into camp. Good news awaited them. The French Army had withdrawn from Mexico and Libbie sighed with relief that danger from that source had vanished. Soon they had a brief visit from General Sheridan. He complimented Custer on the condition of his men and horses after their long overland march and said that, because of changed conditions in Mexico, they were to go next to Austin, Texas, not Houston. He also promised that he himself would recommend that Custer's rank of Major General be made permanent.

Father Custer joined them and, a little later, Nettie Humphrey, now the wife of Custer's adjutant, Captain Jacob Greene. The two girls had a joyful reunion, while the boisterous practical jokes Father Custer played on his two boys, returned always with good measure, kept things in a mirthful uproar.

For quarters in Hempstead the Custers had a large tent with a floor, to Libbie's great satisfaction. The soldiers built a bower of pine-branches to shade it, extending far enough so that it formed a sort of porch. Snakes and insects still abounded, however, and Libbie still preferred to sleep in the wagon. The Greenes' tent was nearby, as were Eliza's quarters and her cooking tent.

At last there was plenty of fresh, clean water, and Eliza made the most of it by a week-long orgy of washing. She ruled that it was proper for Libbie and the General to wear white clothing on Sundays, just as her "old Miss" used to do, proudly spread her laundry on the trees and bushes to dry, and ironed it on an old sheet held down on the grass by rocks.

The neighbors proved to be surprisingly hospitable. The wife of the planter on whose land they were encamped learned that the Custers' only furniture consisted of two camp stools and a bucket, and she sent over some chairs, along with gifts of milk, butter, vegetables, jelly, and a roast of mutton. A seat with a back to it seemed indescribable luxury to Libbie, and it was soon followed by the arrival of a mattress stuffed with specially treated moss, guaranteed to be free of living creatures!

It was on a visit to the planter's home that Libbie saw herself in a mirror for the first time. Her small looking glass had been broken early on the march, and for weeks she had had to dress and arrange her hair by "feel." She stared in unbelieving horror at her image. Where was the complexion of snow and roses, the shining, lustrous hair of which she had been so proud? Her face was darkly burnt by the Texas sun, her hair dull, faded and streaked.

She wanted to burst into tears then and there. "Why didn't you tell me how horrid I looked?" she demanded of her husband.

He took her face between his hands. "Horrid? Don't ever dare speak that way about my Libbie!" he said, and added teasingly, "White or black, you're the loveliest thing in all the world to me!"

The Texans were great hunters and fine shots, and Custer's enthusiasm and skill soon brought him invitations to join their frequent deer hunts. Before long he had accumulated a pack of hounds and was practicing the notes with which to summon them on a hollow steer's horn. The deer hunts were considered too strenuous for ladies, but Libbie was invited one night to accompany a coon hunt and she rode with the best of them through thickets and over ditches until their return at two o'clock in the morning. She had made herself a new riding habit to replace the threadbare and weather-stained one she had worn on the march and, in spite of her sunburnt face, found herself the center of compliments from the gallant Texans.

The pleasure of their stay in camp at Hempstead was marred by two calamities. The first was a "Texas norther," a gale of wind accompanied by an abrupt fall in temperature, which blew down many tents and destroyed the shade of pine-boughs. The second was an epidemic of the dreaded malaria, the "ague," to which even Custer succumbed. He was a rebellious patient, and Libbie had to use all her wiles to get him to take the bitter doses of quinine the doctor prescribed.

In November the Division resumed the march toward the capital city of Austin. Their route lay through arid country where little grew but thickets of mesquite and prickly-pear cactus. Libbie was surprised and entranced, however, by the costumes and equipment of the Texan riders whom they met on the way. They wore broad-brimmed hats, embroidered and beruffled shirts, and bright-hued Mexican serapes, while their saddles, bridles, and stirrup-covers were of elaborately stamped leather adorned with silver. Above all, their fine, blooded horses delighted her.

For headquarters in Austin, Custer was given a large stone building that had been used for an asylum for the blind, and Libbie said a regretful farewell to her traveling wagon-bed. As in Hempstead, they found many of the citizens friendly and hospitable. Armstrong soon acquired more hunting dogs and some excellent horses, among them an extra mount for Libbie.

After the day's work of administering the far-reaching command was over, they spent their evenings as before, riding through the countryside. Libbie even ventured to give parties to which she invited those citizens who had entertained them. The long parlors were decorated with evergreens and flags and lit by myriads of candles, the floors were waxed and a stringband, organized among the soldiers, played for dancing. Giving a dinner was more difficult, since much of their china and glassware had broken during the marches.

After a number of successful entertainments over which Eliza had worked heroically, she came to Libbie with a request. "The colored folks hereabouts have been showing me such hospitality that I'd like a chance to return it," she said.

"Of course! What a fine idea!" Libbie agreed. Armstrong gave his consent and soon invitation-cards written in the fancy penmanship of the regimental clerk went out in Eliza's name, with the word "dancing" in the left-hand corner.

The floors were polished once again, windows, chimneys, columns garlanded with greens, candles lighted and a fine supper spread out on the tables. When the guests arrived Eliza moved happily among them, queen of the occasion, while the fiddles made lively music and the floor shook with the dancing.

Soon Christmas arrived. A shopping trip to San Antonio had supplied presents brought from Old Mexico, the house was decorated once again, a fine large Christmas tree stood in a corner and Armstrong played Santa Claus to the children of the post. Over the doorways hung branches of mistletoe, to the feigned dismay of the ladies and the open delight of the junior officers.

On January 31 news arrived that Custer's permanent commission of Major General had not been confirmed. He was now reduced to the rank of captain again. Libbie was disappointed and indignant, but he refused to be depressed. "Something's bound to turn up, and at least we'll be able to go back home while we wait for orders," he told her.

They set about packing their few belongings, gave away most of the twenty-three dogs Armstrong had accumulated, sold all his horses except four—Libbie's Custis Lee, the beautiful black Phil Sheridan, the war-horse named Jack Rucker, and Fanchon, the racing mare he had bought in Texas.

They traveled by rail to Galveston, then boarded a steamer for New Orleans. The voyage was stormy and everyone was deathly seasick. Once in New Orleans they quickly recovered, but in that fashionable city Libbie learned that her clothes were all woefully out of style. Armstrong insisted upon taking her on a tour of New Orleans' wonderful shops to buy a new wardrobe. "But we can't afford it, Autie," she protested. "You'll have only a captain's pay from now on and it's a quarter of what you had before. We should try to be economical."

"We've saved up almost a thousand dollars," he assured her confidently. "I want my pretty little wife to look her best when we get home to Monroe." Happily she bought what he selected for her and they dined, as before, in the finest restaurants of the glamorous old city.

Then up the Mississippi by steamer and home by rail to Monroe at last. Their welcome was everything Libbie had

dreamed of, except for Mrs. Bacon's open horror at sight of
her daughter's tanned face. "However could you have allowed
her to ruin her exquisite complexion?" she demanded of
Armstrong. "It was her greatest beauty—and look at it now!"

After the first festivities of their welcome were over, offers
of all kinds began to pour in to Custer. Business companies
and financial institutions were flatteringly eager to use the
prestige of his name as one of their officials. He was assured
by many that the reputation he had won during the War
would carry him far in politics. A diplomatic post was hinted
at for him by someone influential in the Federal Government.

From another source he learned that a group of prominent
Mexicans were looking for a top-ranking cavalry officer to
aid them in their fight to expel the Emperor Maximilian and
restore their Republic. He would have the rank of Adjutant
General of their army and receive a fabulously large salary.

This last opportunity interested and excited Custer, although Libbie's heart failed her at the thought of another war.
He decided to apply for the position and General Grant himself sent a letter of recommendation full of high praise. He
asked for leave of absence from the Army; it was refused by
the War Department. He would have to resign his commission, he was told, and this he was reluctant to do. Com-
missions, even that of captain, were hard to get now that
the Civil War was over. The Mexican position might last
only a year or so and after that, what? He had heard that
new regiments of cavalry were being formed for service on
the Plains, and that he had a good chance of assignment to
one of them, with promotion.

Custer traveled to New York and Washington, seeking
advice on what decision to make. He was welcomed and
entertained everywhere he went and he wrote enthusiastic

letters back to Libbie, who had remained in Monroe partly for economy's sake and partly to be with her parents after so long a separation.

Judge Bacon seemed distressingly feeble to her. One evening while he was lying on his couch, he spoke to her about her husband's career. "Armstrong is a born soldier," he said. "That's where his career lies. Don't try to change him, Libbie."

"But he would be safe, out of the Army," she protested. "And how wonderful to have a quiet, permanent home, perhaps here in Monroe!"

"Safe, perhaps, but happy?" he asked. "I doubt very much if a quiet, permanent home is what Armstrong truly desires. No, he's a soldier, my dear. Never forget that."

A few days later the Judge fell ill and, on May 16, 1866, he passed away almost without warning. Custer hurried back to Monroe to be with Libbie during the sad ceremonies, then, when all was over, he took her with him to Washington.

President Johnson was arranging a journey to Illinois to lay the cornerstone of a monument to Stephen A. Douglas and to place a wreath on Abraham Lincoln's tomb. He hoped to use this opportunity to explain his reconstruction policy to the people, the policy of "malice toward none, of charity for all" which Lincoln had proposed. He would be accompanied by members of his cabinet and distinguished officers of the Army and Navy. General and Mrs. Custer were invited to join the party. Although now officially only a captain, Custer still retained his courtesy title of General.

This swing around the circle began pleasantly enough with a trip aboard a special steamer up the Hudson to visit West Point. The radical Republicans, who disagreed with President Johnson's desire to treat the conquered South humanely, spoiled the remainder of the trip. His pleas that passion and prejudice be laid aside were met with hostility by crowds gathered to hear him. They cheered the war-heroes, Grant, Farragut, and Custer, and gave some heed to Secretaries Seward and Gideon Welles. Political bosses even approached Custer with offers to back him for office.

The President was received more and more discourteously every day and soon hecklers in the crowd began to create disturbances. Hostile newspapers printed insults and downright lies: in Ohio the attacks were especially vicious and there were even threats against the party in the street.

Custer, who agreed wholeheartedly with Johnson, was furious. He tried to defend him, but in his efforts at speechmaking his words tumbled out far too fast to be understood and when he lost his temper his voice rose to shrillness. At Scio he came stamping back into the ladies' car where Libbie waited, his blue eyes blazing. "I grew up only a few miles from this town, but I'll never willingly set foot here again!" he declared.

Sadly disillusioned with politics, the Custers left the Presidential party at Steubenville and returned to Monroe. Word had come that Armstrong had been assigned to a newly formed regiment, the Seventh Cavalry, and had been promoted to Lieutenant-colonel. Their post would be Fort Riley, Kansas, far out on the Great Plains at the very end of the railroad. Distant and desolate though it might be, it still seemed preferable to the sordid world of politics they had glimpsed so briefly.

To pack their clothes and the few belongings they were taking with them was a simple matter. Eliza was to go along with them, as was a small Negro boy who had attached himself to Custer in Texas as a jockey. Johnny Cisco pleaded to be taken, too, but Custer insisted on placing the boy in a school. "He's far too bright a lad not to be given a chance in life," he said.

There were the horses, and the dogs also: Turk, a huge, homely English bulldog and Byron, a beautiful grayhound, and a pack of other hounds too, for Armstrong had heard reports of splendid hunting to be found on the wild frontier. As for Libbie, she was looking forward to this journey with special anticipation. She had persuaded one of her school friends to go with them, a gay, curly-haired blonde named Anna, who preferred to be called by the more fashionable "Diana" and who was the reigning belle of Monroe. What was more, they planned to stop on the way at the famous World's Fair in St. Louis. Some Detroit friends had engaged a private car for an excursion to the Fair and invited the Custer party to ride with them.

The Fair was all that had been advertised, and more. Libbie and Autie and their friends visited every corner of the grounds, watched the tournament of horsemanship in the great amphitheatre and the crowning of the Queen of Love and Beauty by the victorious knight. As a climax, they danced at the grand ball held in her honor.

One evening they attended a theatre where the young actor, Lawrence Barrett was playing in a sentimental comedy *Rosedale*. Custer was so delighted with his performance that he requested a meeting with Mr. Barrett to thank him, and it was the beginning of a warm friendship between the two men.

The few days of gay interlude in St. Louis came to an end and they took up their journey again to Fort Leavenworth, Kansas. In that thriving frontier town they paused long enough to buy supplies, most important of all a cook-stove for Eliza. Then aboard the train and westward to where the workmen were still busy laying the tracks, some ten miles from Fort Riley.

They alighted from the train to learn that General Sherman was at the Fort. That very day he had driven the final spike to finish that division of the tracks, on the invitation of the railroad company. An ambulance for them to ride in and a wagon for their luggage was at the station to take them to Fort Riley. They climbed aboard and Libbie and Diana clung as best they could to the slippery, oilcloth-covered seats during the rough journey while they peered out with awe and wonder at the vast panorama of sky and plain that surrounded them on every side.

Fort Riley was situated on a wide plateau at the meeting of the Republican and Smoky Hill Rivers. Libbie had expected that a fort would be built with high stone walls, towers, and a moat such as she had seen at Fortress Monroe, and the thought of such protection against the hostile Indians had been very comforting. Instead she saw a quadrangle of low, story-and-a-half buildings set around a parade ground in the midst of the empty plain. Other structures, the sutler's store, quartermaster and commissary storehouses, and stables stood nearby. That was all. No town, no trees, no bushes, nothing whatever except the sea of low-curling buffalo grass, now reddish yellow with fall coloring and stretching away, mile on mile, toward the setting sun.

At the entrance to the quadrangle they halted. "I'll go in and report to the officer in command," Armstrong said, jumping to the ground. "You'd better keep Turk and Byron in there with you girls or they'll begin to fight," he added, as he strode off.

Without their master's authoritative voice to keep them in order, the two dogs did just that. Diana had to cling with all her strength to Byron's collar at one end of the ambulance while Libbie dragged the enormous Turk on to her lap and held him, growling and struggling, at the other end of the wagon, during the long wait for Armstrong to return.

Tired, hungry, dusty and travel-stained, they at last climbed from the ambulance to learn that no quarters whatever were ready for them. All five would have to be guests of Mrs. Gibbs, wife of the acting commander of the garrison. Since General Sherman was already there occupying the only guest-room, Major and Mrs. Gibbs were having to give up their own bedroom to the Custers.

Distressed at the imposition, Libbie tried to protest. "Don't give it the slightest thought, my dear," Mrs. Gibbs told her, smiling. "You'll soon learn that this is the way of life on a frontier post. There's simply no place else to go. We're delighted to have you here and very happy that you've arrived safely."

Red-whiskered General Sherman took Libbie's hand. "I've heard that you're a fine horsewoman, Mrs. Custer," he said. "This is the best place in all the world to ride. Child, you'll find that the air on these plains is like champagne. There's nothing else to compare it with."

The next morning the Custer luggage and belongings were unloaded into one of the houses on officer's row which was being vacated by a departing family. Their few pieces of furniture looked meager and lonely in the bare, echoing rooms. However, they were able to buy a few articles from an officer who was leaving, and others were manufactured from boxes and boards and were covered and cushioned with calico. Serapes brought from Texas added color, unbleached muslin curtained the windows, and heavy army blankets served for rugs. Soon the place seemed habitable to the newcomers.

"It's really cozy," Diana insisted, while Libbie, looking about her with shining eyes, breathed, "It's home!"

Colonel A. J. Smith, the commanding officer of the Seventh Cavalry, arrived soon after they did. He was a grizzled veteran of the Mexican War and much Plains fighting as well as of the Civil War. He at once turned over the work of whipping the newly formed regiment into shape to Custer, his second in command.

Armstrong soon found that the enlisted men were a mixed lot. There were a few veterans among them, but some of the others were newly arrived immigrants, healthy and sturdy enough but able to speak very little English. Another large group were former Confederate soldiers who were touchy and resentful of authority. Numbers of the men, moreover, had joined up only to get free transportation across the country with the purpose of deserting at the first opportunity and going on to seek their fortunes in the newly opened Colorado mines. Few had any cavalry experience and the mounts which arrived for them were largely wild and unbroken. Nevertheless Custer set to work with undaunted enthusiasm and energy. "I'm going to make this into the best regiment on the plains," he vowed to Libbie.

As for the officers, those assigned to the Seventh slowly arrived one by one, while those transferred from the Fort to other posts departed. It was almost spring before the staff seemed to have any unity. Armstrong succeeded in his efforts to have Tom, now an officer with two Congressional Medals of Honor, ordered to this outfit and with him his old friend George Yates. Others among the new officers were Captain Louis Hamilton, a grandson of the famous Alexander, Captain Myles Keogh, a jovial Irish soldier of fortune who had won distinction at Gettysburg, and Lieutenant Nowlan, another Irishman. Canadian-born Lieutenant Cooke was an expert shot, with the most luxuriant side-whiskers in the command, and Captain Frederick Benteen was white-haired and fresh-faced, but with a sharp and sardonic tongue. He was an efficient, experienced cavalry officer but from the first he resented the fact that Custer, six years his junior, so far outranked him.

Early in their stay Libbie learned that life on an Army post presented unexpected problems. "Darling, weren't you less than cordial to that captain's wife who called here this afternoon?" Custer asked her one evening.

"Oh but Autie, surely you know why. She's—well, she's really *not* a lady!"

"She's an officer's wife, Libbie. In a small, isolated post like this it's essential to maintain pleasant relations with everyone—I mean everyone. It's well known that many an officer's career has been ruined because his wife wasn't able to do that."

Libbie listened to him in dismay. Could she ever be guilty of harming his career? She drew a long breath. "I promise to remember that, *always*," she assured him.

As soon as they were settled a fine little sorrel horse was obtained for Diana. At once she was booked for rides weeks ahead by the admiring bachelor officers, with the result that Libbie had little chance to enjoy her friend's company while riding. Riding with Autie was all that Libbie really cared about, however, and soon she was sensing to the utmost the flawless joy of skimming at top speed over the limitless, springy turf of the Plains. "It's too wonderful to describe. I think I never breathed a full breath of air before this!" she told Armstrong. "General Sherman said that the air here is like champagne and I'll bet it has almost the same effect!"

They were galloping close together, their horses abreast, stride for stride. Suddenly Armstrong leaned over, encircled Libbie's slim waist with his arm and lifted her out of the saddle. He held her suspended above her galloping horse for what seemed long to her but was only a few moments, then set her in the saddle again, breathless, and laughing. Her confidence in him was so complete that it never occurred to her to be frightened—until afterwards.

Fall passed and winter approached, bringing gales of wind that carried dust and sand everywhere. It penetrated the doors and windows, coated the floors and furniture, got into the clothing and food, everything. It stung the eyes and nostrils and they even tasted it, gritty between their teeth. To cross the parade ground became an ordeal for Libbie and Diana, whose full skirts billowed up over their heads without warning until they learned from Mrs. Gibbs to sew bags of lead shot into the hems to hold them down.

After weeks of incessant wind they woke one morning to the soft silent whiteness of snow. An immense blanket of arctic cold had settled over the Plains, slowing everything to a numbing ache. The wood stoves were kept going full blast, but they only served to toast the side next to them to blisters while leaving the other side still icy and shivering.

For a time the weather was too severe even for Custer to ride out with his dogs, and when his duties for the day were finished he paced their quarters like a caged panther. "What in the world is there to do, Libbie?" he demanded.

After the excitement of his Virginia campaigns and of Texas, no wonder he found this dull imprisonment unendurable, she thought, her heart aching for him. He loved to read, but the Regiment was too new to have accumulated any sort of library, and the few books they had been able to fit into their baggage were soon read through. There would be no papers or magazines for weeks to come.

"Why don't you write down some of your war experiences?" Libbie suggested one day. "They should be recorded, and perhaps a publisher might be interested in them."

His face brightened. "That's a fine idea," he said. "Come, sit here beside me, Libbie. I'm going to become an author!" She spent many afternoons and evenings, after that, sewing beside the desk where he covered sheet after sheet of paper with his rapid scrawl, then read them over for her approval.

Among his first acts, Custer had organized a regimental band, and now it showed its value by serving nobly to pass the time. It gave music for the improvised entertainments with which the isolated garrison whiled away the winter months. There were so few women that every one of them, married or not, of any age, was a belle. "It will be a wonder if I'm not thoroughly spoiled," Libbie laughed one day. "I have more invitations to ride and to dance now than when I was a girl in Monroe. As many, actually, as Diana!"

"Accept them all, Libbie," Custer told her. "Only remember not to seem to give preference to any one. That will avoid gossip—and also keep your husband from getting jealous!"

Eliza, too, received much attention, especially just after mealtime, when the back door of the Custers' quarters seemed always to be a gathering place for soldiers. Her handouts of cookies, hot biscuits and apple-dumplings became famous. She was especially generous to the squads of prisoners who went about under guard cleaning up the post. They brought pathetic tales to her of undeserved wrongs, which she relayed, with dramatic embellishments, to Libbie and Diana. Together the three then hurried to Custer with emotional pleas for "justice" for young men who, too often, proved to be graceless scamps and more than deserved their punishments.

Libbie found it easy to belittle and ignore the discomforts of winter, for Autie was with her. She knew that spring would bring something far worse for her to endure. The flood of white settlers pouring West and the coming of the railroads were alarming and angering the Plains Indians. They protested that the white man was breaking treaties, and when their protests had no effect, they began to raid isolated ranches, settlements, wagon trains and stage stations and even to hamper the work of the railroad crews.

News had come that as soon as weather permitted, troops from Fort Leavenworth would march out to join the Seventh in a campaign against the hostile tribes of the region, the Kiowas, Arapahoes, Cheyennes, Comanches and the Sioux. These Indian warriors were reported to be skillful fighting men, Libbie learned, as dangerous as any Confederate Cavalry, and far more savage and cruel.

CHAPTER

12

Late in March the infantry from Fort Leavenworth arrived under General Hancock, who was to command the whole expedition. Armstrong was in the highest of spirits. "They have the well-known journalist, Henry M. Stanley along, representing New York and eastern papers, and an artist, Theodore Davis, from *Harper's Weekly*. This affair will be well publicized. Even out here at the end of nowhere we're still important to the country and whatever success we have won't go unnoticed," he said, as he kissed Libbie goodbye. "I'll write to you by every courier. Remember, darling, no tears!"

A trumpet rang out, the band struck up the rollicking notes of "The Girl I Left Behind Me," Custer swung into the saddle and was gone. Libbie bit her lips to stop their trembling and managed to smile and wave until he was out of sight. Then she turned and fled to her room. A cold, black cloud of depression settled over her. The discomfort of their quarters, the bleakness of the empty plains, barely relieved by hesitant signs of spring, the moaning, incessant wind, the ever-present fear of savage enemies who lurked about their small island of safety came sweeping down upon her. Autie's gay confidence, had kept them all at bay. Now that he was gone she was helpless before them.

Except for a few troopers of the Seventh left to guard their supplies, infantry soldiers now manned the post, and the difference was noticeable at once to Libbie. No clatter of horses' hoofs, no cheerful sounds from the stables, no jingle of spurs or clank of sabres, the tamer notes of bugle and drum instead of stirring trumpet-calls. Pretty Diana soon had a string of beaux from among the infantry officers and Eliza, too, from the colored soldiers newly arrived from the South. The days were as busy and lively as ever for them, but for Libbie they dragged endlessly from one mail's arrival to the next.

True to his promise, Armstrong's letters were frequent, and when she was poring over one of them she felt relief from her anxiety. Sometimes he wrote so many pages that they had burst through their envelope and were tied together with string when they reached her. They were always cheerful and buoyant, full of colorful descriptions of the march and of camp life.

He had found a good cook among the soldiers, but not so good as Eliza, he wrote. The three horses, Phil Sheridan, Custis Lee and Fanchon were behaving well. The dogs were too, but they were still hopelessly baffled by prairie dogs. Custis Lee had surprised himself the other evening. He was enjoying his usual roll on the ground after his saddle had been removed, but he had started it too close to a river-bank, with the result that he had slid over the edge of a little bluff and into the water. There was never a more amazed-looking horse!

As for Indians, he wrote of a council which General Hancock had held with a group of Sioux and Cheyenne chiefs. These were the first "wild" Indians Custer had ever met, and his description of their appearance was vivid—paint, feathers, gaudy-colored blankets, beads, and silver ornaments. They were impressive-looking warriors, he wrote, and their swift, nimble ponies drew his admiration too.

The council had seemed friendly, and the chiefs promised to meet again to finish settling some matters. The troops arrived at the next meeting-place and waited there for the Indians to come from the village which they could see beyond a clump of trees. They waited long past the hour appointed. Then Custer, with some scouts, was sent to learn the reason for the delay. The Indians had all disappeared, leaving their tepees standing there empty.

General Hancock had been furious. He ordered Custer to take the Seventh Cavalry out and round the savages up. "The scouts tell me we have little chance of finding them," Armstrong wrote. "When pursued they scatter like quail all over the prairie, and their light little ponies can live off the country and travel faster than our horses. However, I have been known to do some fast traveling myself, and I perhaps shall surprise them!"

Meanwhile a series of unexpected dangers threatened Fort Riley. The first was a prairie fire in the sea of tinder-dry grass, so sudden, so fierce that it was upon them before even the sentries saw it. In a matter of moments the whole earth and sky seemed to be ablaze. The garrison was called out to fight it with brooms, blankets, anything they could find, but nothing but a miraculous change in the wind saved the structures of the Fort from certain destruction.

The next danger was brief but equally terrifying. One quiet afternoon Libbie heard a strange rumbling noise, as though a great cavalcade of wagons were stampeding across the parade ground. The next instant the floor began to rock under her and the pictures on the walls to swing. It was an earthquake! No real damage was done, but it was an experience not to be forgotten.

Then, a few weeks later, mutiny broke out among the infantry soldiers. The men, almost all new recruits, lacked discipline and the officer in charge was a mild-mannered man who was unable to establish his authority. Eliza moved her sleeping-quarters upstairs with Libbie and Diana, while Diana got herself a pistol and practiced her marksmanship. At last word of this state of affairs reached General Hancock. He sent Major Gibbs back to take command of the garrison and, under him, order soon prevailed.

Custer's letters continued to be optimistic. He made little of any danger, but stories reached Libbie from other sources which distressed and alarmed her. Custis Lee, her favorite horse, had been accidentally shot during a buffalo hunt. The regiment had come upon a stage station which had been recently attacked by Indians: the men in charge had been massacred with horrible tortures. Six travelers on the Republican River had been surrounded and killed soon after. Sheltered for a short time at the Fort was a woman passenger on another stage coach which had been under attack. She told of her harrowing experience, crouched in the bottom of the coach while the Indians kept up a running fight beside them.

"At least we Army women can always be sure of an armed escort of soldiers," Libbie said later to Mrs. Gibbs.

"If she had been the wife of an officer of the Seventh under military escort when they were attacked, she would not have lived to tell the tale," Mrs. Gibbs told her soberly.

"What do you mean?" Libbie asked, startled.

"Our officers have all given their words of honor to each other that if ever one of them has a fellow-officer's wife in his charge and is attacked by Indians, he will shoot her dead at once rather than run the risk of her falling into the hands of the savages," was the answer. "Didn't your husband tell you that?"

Libbie stared in shocked horror. "No!" she answered. "But surely they would never, never really do such a cruel thing!"

"Not cruel—kind and merciful," the older woman said. "My husband has told me of what he has had to look at when they arrived too late at the scene of an Indian massacre. What happened to the women was too horrible to repeat."

The next letter from the expedition brought wonderful news. Custer wrote that the cavalry was back from its long scout and was going into camp at Fort Hays. Could Libbie come and join him there? Her heart soared like a rocket and she began to pack her bag and make her plans at once.

General Sherman, as it happened, was traveling by train from Fort Riley to Fort Harker, where the railroad now ended. Libbie told him of her wish and he invited her, with Diana and Eliza, to ride in his private car with his party. There would be a journey after that of eighty miles from there to Fort Hays, but what was eighty miles to Libbie if Armstrong was to be at the end of it?

Libbie and her companions spent the night at Fort Harker, a forlorn little post consisting of rough log huts roofed with sod. In the morning they joined a party traveling, with a large escort of soldiers, in the now familiar ambulances. They stopped every ten or fifteen miles at stage stations built to shelter relays of horses. These were huddles of log huts and dugouts barricaded by wooden shutters heavy enough to resist Indian attacks.

Though the final miles were made under looming thunderclouds, the journey was over at last. The huts of Fort Hays appeared in the distance and, along the stream beyond the Fort, Libbie saw flashes of white canvas through the cottonwood trees. The encampment of the Seventh Cavalry, with Autie there waiting to lift her down from the ambulance and into his arms!

The storm burst almost at the moment of their arrival, and during the night it increased, with wind, thunder, and continuous blazing sheet-lightning such as Libbie had never experienced before. In the midst of it their tent blew down and Libbie would have been thoroughly drenched if Armstrong had not rolled her into a blanket and carried her through the downpour to the next tent. Her clothing was so soaked that she had to go about all the next day in Autie's underwear under one of Diana's dresses, and with a pair of his cavalry boots clumping on her feet. No calamity seemed of any consequence to Libbie now, however. It was all hilarious fun with Autie there to laugh it away.

The happy weeks of their reunion were marred by trouble and near-mutiny among the soldiers over the food they had found waiting for them at the post. "I don't blame them at all," Custer told Libbie. "It's disgraceful. The rations stored here have been here since the War—the date 1860 was on one of the boxes of moldy biscuit. There were even flat stones packed between the layers of bacon to give it weight. Men who would do that to the soldiers of their own Army are far worse than any Indians!"

Custer staged a buffalo hunt and secured some fresh meat for his men, but the rations he had requested had still not arrived when orders came for him to start off on another scout against the Indians. "We'll have to cross the road that leads to the Colorado mines on our way," he said. "Some of the men, I'm told, have said that they mean to desert there. They'll find themselves in real trouble if they try!"

Once again Libbie watched the wagon train and the mounted troopers disappear over the empty horizon. Armstrong had delayed as long as he could to make sure that their tent was well-anchored against the wind, then galloped after his command. "If there's any chance of our settling down in one place, say Fort McPherson, I'll send for you," he promised.

This time I shan't cry, Libbie vowed to herself, but she felt the tears come as soon as he was gone.

A strong detachment of infantry guarded the post, for it was plain that hostile Indians were all around. Stray shots at the sentries and almost nightly efforts to stampede and drive away the horses and mules kept everyone on the alert. The women were ordered to stay strictly within the limits of the camp, and as the days passed the restrictions grew more and more tedious. One evening Diana persuaded a young lieutenant to take them for a walk to gather wild flowers along the rolling bluffs. They went farther than they had intended and it was twilight when they arrived at the camp.

The first notice they had that a sentry had sighted them was the whistle of bullets over their heads. In the distance and the dim light the guard mistook them for approaching Indians!

"Get down!" the officer ordered. "Lie as flat as you can until I can crawl close enough to tell him who we are."

The two girls flung themselves to the ground and practically burrowed into the grass. "Oh Libbie, I seem to make such a high target! If only I were as thin as you!" moaned Diana, until now so proud of her attractively rounded figure.

It was only a few moments, although it seemed like hours, before the lieutenant convinced the sentry that they were friends. The girls were helped to their feet and hurried into camp. "No more walks for you, Miss Libbie!" Eliza scolded. "And you'd better not let the Ginnel know about this or you'll be back at Fort Riley, quick as scat!"

Writing letters and waiting for infrequent couriers to bring Armstrong's letters to her were now the only way Libbie found to pass the days. One morning she had a brief, dazzling moment of hope. Lieutenant Cooke, of Custer's command, arrived with a wagon train for supplies and brought word for Libbie to travel back with him to Fort McPherson, where Custer was now encamped. She had her satchel packed and ready when word came that the commanding officer of their post refused to let her go. "I'm sorry, Mrs. Custer, but there's a scout just come in with a report that a big war party of Cheyennes is on the loose somewhere in the territory you'd have to cross. I know that your husband would approve of my decision," he stated.

Libbie remembered what Mrs. Gibbs had said of the officers' vow to each other. Somehow, however, all danger seemed unreal to her when she would be traveling *toward* Armstrong, and it was with a rebellious heart that she unpacked her little bag.

After that came several days and nights of rain. Libbie and Diana were awakened suddenly in the stormy darkness by the shout of a sentry. "The creek! The creek's flooding!" he yelled.

In a matter of moments an officer was at the opening of their tent. "Mrs. Custer! Miss Diana! Get up at once. The creek's rising so fast that we're in for a dangerous flood."

They dressed hurriedly, fumbling in the dark with cold

fingers. The whole camp now was aroused and shouting to each other in the wet blackness. Libbie, Diana, and Eliza emerged from their tents to see, by flashes of lightning, that the creek, formerly a little trickle at the bottom of the gully, now filled it from bank to bank. Tops of trees were bending and swirling in the current. The stream had risen thirty-five feet during the night!

Their own tents were fortunately on high ground and, after making sure that they were safe, the officer hurried away to help save what they could of the rest of the camp. Two of the dogs now took the opportunity to start a fight, and Libbie and Diana were struggling to separate them when suddenly there was a different note in the shouting from upstream—it had become yells of panic and terror.

"Miss Libbie! Look!" Eliza screamed.

Borne along by the current in the midst of swirling debris of logs, brush, and masses of earth, by the almost continuous lightning they could see the figure of a man. Suddenly he caught hold of the branches of a tree and clung there just under the bank where they stood.

"A rope!" Libbie cried. "Get a rope, Eliza. Run and fetch the clothesline from the kitchen tent."

"My clothesline? That's the only good clothesline in all Kansas!" Eliza protested, but nevertheless she ran off and was back in a moment with it in her hands.

"I'll make a loop in it and we'll throw it to him. If he can only catch hold, we can save him," Libbie called through the noise of the storm.

After several heart-rending failures the man was finally able to grasp the rope and anchor it around his body. The task of pulling him out of the terrible, dragging grasp of the current was almost beyond the three women's strength, but

somehow they did it. He was cold and blue and barely able
to stagger when they helped him to their tent and wrapped him
in blankets. Then they hurried back to the task again. They
managed to save two more soldiers, but others were swept
away beyond their reach, and their despairing cries rang in
Libbie's ears long afterward.

Seven men had been lost, caught in their camp on the low
ground before they were aware of the danger. Most of the
tents and equipment and supplies had been swept away. "This
is no place for ladies," the commanding officer declared. "It
will be weeks before we can repair the damage. In the meanwhile I'll have to send you back to Fort Harker."

Two officers and an escort of ten mounted men accompanied the wagons and ambulances which carried them. Libbie
watched the small island in the midst of the plains which was
Camp Hays melt into the landscape. With it, she knew, disappeared her chances of seeing Armstrong for the rest of the
summer.

At the first stage station an ominous sight was waiting. A
stage coach, riddled with bullets, had arrived only the day
before after a fight with Indians. Here, moreover, the troopers
of their escort managed to buy enough adulterated whisky
from one of the station attendants to make themselves
thoroughly drunk. One by one they toppled from their
mounts and had to be lifted into the forage wagons and
carried there during the rest of the trip.

Their horses were tied behind the vehicles and the little
party proceeded with no military guard now except for the
drivers and the two officers, who kept their rifles ready during
the whole nightmarish journey. Buffalo, blacktailed deer,
coyotes, and jackrabbits scurried out of their way, but merci-
fully they saw no Indians. In spite of her constant terror,

Libbie could still be aware of the gorgeous wildflowers which had sprung up after the rain and now covered the earth with an exotic carpet of color.

With only short rests they rode day and night and arrived at Fort Harker so thoroughly exhausted that even those rough huts looked like havens of comfort.

The commanding officer came out to meet them. He looked gaunt and harassed and it was plain that their coming was far from welcome. "We really have no suitable quarters to offer you ladies," he said. "An epidemic of cholera has struck here and we are fighting it as best we can. The sick men and the Sisters of Mercy who are nursing them have filled all the huts. However, some of our officers have offered to give up their tent to you. I'm afraid that's the best we can do."

"Oh, no, we don't want to inconvenience anyone!" Libbie exclaimed. "We can sleep here in our ambulances."

The two vehicles were placed between two buildings and a tarpaulin was stretched over them. Eliza made a campfire, they had a hot meal and went to their beds feeling secure at last from attack by Indians, even if far from safe from the dreaded disease.

During the night a storm came up. The tarpaulin was blown away, rain poured in upon them and, worst of all, the ambulances began to move! They had been placed on a slope and now the wind was pushing the one in which Libbie and Diana lay directly toward the swollen stream. Fortunately a sentry heard their screams in time to rescue them.

The next day the bedraggled little party was put on the train for Fort Riley. Miles farther away from Armstrong, Libbie thought despairingly. It was clear to her, however, that their presence at Fort Harker would be an added burden to the already overworked garrison, and she could not protest.

At Fort Riley Libbie settled down again into the dreary routine of trying to pass the time while she waited for the irregular arrival of letters. The pages continued to be lively, full of accounts of the wildlife they saw and hunted, of a foot-race organized among the men, of smoking a peace pipe with a famous Cheyenne chief called Pawnee Killer, and of a young beaver Autie had tamed for a pet. From others at Fort Riley, Libbie learned less pleasant news. The Indians were growing more formidable and General Hancock had gone back to Fort Leavenworth, acknowledging his campaign a failure. The wagon train under Lieutenant Cooke had been attacked and had to fight its way back to Custer against almost overwhelming numbers of Indian warriors.

If I had been with it! Libbie thought with a freezing shudder.

Custer's fears of his men deserting to the mines had been realized. A large number of them had got away and Armstrong had only prevented more from going by the sternest measures. Worst of all was the fate of the well-liked young Lieutenant Kidder and his men. He had been sent out with orders from General Sherman for Custer. He, his guide, and the ten soldiers with him had been captured and tortured to death by the Indians.

"Don't worry about the Ginnel!" Eliza tried to reassure Libbie. "He has a lot of soldiers with him—lots more than ten!"

Libbie, however, was remembering his habit of riding in advance of the column to scout out the trail and to hunt for game, and her heart was heavy with dread.

A few days later she was sitting in her room in their quarters at Fort Riley sewing, while her mind struggled with agonizing questions. Where was Autie now? What dangers was he facing? Was he even alive? There had been no letter for days. She wanted desperately to go out on the gallery to wait for the mail-carrier, but the thought of another disappointment was more than she could face.

Suddenly there was a sound from outside—the clank of a sabre and the jingle of spurs. A quick, springing, familiar step mounted the stairs. Libbie was on her feet; her sewing slipped to the floor and the spools went rolling into the corners of the room. The door was flung wide to admit a flood of dazzling sunlight. "Autie!" she cried, and was sobbing with joy against his dusty uniform.

He had returned from his long scouting trip to find that Libbie had had to leave Fort Hays for Fort Harker, and that cholera was raging there. Since his men needed supplies and medicines that could only be got at that rail-head, Custer had hurried there to arrange for them and to learn news of her. When he arrived he had been told that she was back at Fort Riley where cholera was falsely reported also. It would take the supply wagons some time to load. He had, therefore, come by train to Fort Riley to make sure that she was safe.

This unauthorized journey to see his wife brought a trial by court-martial to the young officer. Other charges, of harshness toward the deserters and of wearing out men and horses by excessive marches, were added. He was convicted and sentenced to a year's suspension of rank and pay. There was much heated disagreement in the Army as to his guilt. His friends maintained that he had been made a scapegoat for the failure of General Hancock's campaign, while his enemies murmured their satisfaction that the flamboyant "Boy General" was at last brought low.

As for Libbie, she was to write of their meeting, long afterward, "There was in that summer of 1867 one long, perfect day. It was mine—blessed be our memory, for it preserves to us the joys as well as the sadness of life!—it is still mine, for time and for eternity."

CHAPTER

13

To Libbie the whole affair of the court-martial and the conviction seemed monstrously unjust, the work of small-minded men who were jealous of her husband's youth and fame. Taking her cue from Armstrong, however, she kept her head high and her outward appearance cheerful. "Armstrong merited acquittal," she wrote to Rebecca Richmond. "However, we are not disturbed, for now we can be together for a year and a half, for the next Indian campaign will be over by summer of next year and by the time we return the regiment will be in winter quarters. We are the wonder of the garrison here, we are in such spirits."

It was impossible in any case for the buoyant Custer to be downcast for long. "I am like Micawber, waiting for something to turn up," he wrote to a friend. "In the meantime I am writing a memoir of my experiences from West Point to Appomattox, arranged for with Harper and Brothers."

The Custers remained for a short time after the trial at Fort Leavenworth, then journeyed home to Monroe, and for that year, 1867-68, Libbie was again among her old friends and schoolmates. The house was strange without the presence of her father, but the Custer family lived only a short block away, and Libbie was delighted to find that Armstrong's sister, Maggie, was growing up into an attractive girl, blonde, curly-haired and lively as her brothers.

Armstrong worked for a while at his Civil War memoirs, then, at the request of the publishers, turned to writing about the Plains and the Indian campaign for the *Galaxy Magazine*. "You write so well," General Sherman told him in a letter, "that people are saying it's your wife, not you, who's the author."

To which Custer replied, "Then they should give me credit, all the same, for being able to choose such a wife."

The disgrace of the court-martial seemed to have little effect upon his popularity with the public. It was not mentioned in the accounts of Hancock's campaign printed in Harper's, although he figured large in the story. He was still the dashing, romantic figure of the War with the added luster of a new background, the limitless, Indian-imperiled plains toward which the eyes of the country now were turning.

On September 24, 1868, when Custer's sentence still had months to run, he received a telegram from his old leader, General Sheridan. The spring before, Sheridan had been appointed Military Commander of the Department of the Missouri, and the wire came from Fort Hays. "Generals Sherman, Sully and myself and nearly all the officers of your regiment have asked for you and I hope the application will be successful," the telegram read. "Can you come at once?"

Armstrong read the wire, then whooped aloud. "*Can* I come? Libbie, I'm going back to my regiment!" He snatched her out of her chair, whirled her around until she was dizzy, then set her on top of a high cabinet of books. "Stay there out of my way while I pack!"

"But Autie, you haven't had your orders yet from Washington!" she protested, as soon as she could catch her breath.

"Oh, they'll be along soon. Wait—first I'd better go down to the telegraph office and wire my answer to Sheridan," he said, and was striding toward the door when she called out frantically to remind him to get her off her perch before he left.

"Can I go West with you, Autie?" she pleaded as he swung her to the floor.

But he shook his head. "Not at this time, darling. I'm in too much of a hurry now, but I'll send for you as soon as I learn what Sheridan's plans are. I promise."

He took the next train for the West, along with his three new dogs—two staghounds and a pointer—and Libbie found herself left with only his promise to cling to. How swiftly the happy security of their life in Monroe had been shattered! But the light that Sheridan's telegram had kindled in her husband's face told her only too clearly how much it meant to him to return to the life of action he loved.

"Don't you worry, Miss Libbie. Fall's coming and you know they don't fight Indians this time of year. The Ginnel'll be sending for you directly," Eliza told her. "Might as well begin to pack right away."

The welcome summons came soon after. Libbie learned that she and Eliza were to remain at Fort Leavenworth, however, for Armstrong was already on the march. Sheridan had evolved a new plan for dealing with the Indians. During the whole of the preceding summer his troops had been in the field under General Sully, but they had had no more success against the red men than had Hancock. In a period of two months, Indian war parties had swept out of nowhere and killed one hundred and twenty-four settlers in Sheridan's department, while the disgruntled, heavily loaded cavalrymen plodded fruitlessly after them. To add to the troopers' dissatisfaction, General Sully had proved to be no horseman and had actually led his men while traveling in an ambulance! The effect of all this on the morale of the Seventh Cavalry was disastrous.

Now Sheridan had decided to attack the Indians in the winter, when they were holed up in their permanent cold-weather camps and while their ponies, which lived so successfully off the grass in the summer, would be weak from lack of forage. The scouts had learned that most of the hostile Cheyennes, Comanches, Arapahoes, and Kiowas who had done the raiding were located somewhere along the Washita River in the Oklahoma Territory, and Sheridan planned to send a strong column to attack them there.

Most of his best advisers, including the veteran Kit Carson, warned the general that the cavalry could not survive in that frozen wilderness, but he was stubbornly determined to make the attempt. "If anyone can accomplish it, it's Custer," he declared, and thereupon sent for his favorite.

Armstrong's long letters, sent by courier to Fort Leavenworth, kept Libbie posted on the campaign. He told of his reunion with Sheridan and his regiment, and the drills, target and signal practice he arranged for his soldiers to get them in shape for action. He was reassigning the horses by their color to companies to give the regiment a smarter appearance, in an effort to raise its morale. His dogs had proved their courage against wolves. The camp tailor was making him a suit of fur, and buffalo-hide shoes. He expressed admiration and liking for the Osage Indian scouts he had hired, and described the good looks, courage and skill of Sheridan's young dispatch rider, William F. Cody, and also the drollery and independence of two white scouts, California Joe and Jack Corbin.

Soon Armstrong's letters stopped, for the regiment was traveling through early-season snowstorms into untracked wilderness. At last, after a long, anxious wait, news reached Fort Leavenworth that the Seventh Cavalry had scored a decisive victory. They had surprised a large Cheyenne village encamped on the Washita River, late in November. Following Sheridan's stern orders, they had killed all the warriors and captured the women and children. When the lodges, with all the Indians' belongings, food supply, and pony herd, had been destroyed, the regiment returned in triumph to the supply camp where Sheridan waited, flags flying and band blaring out the favorite new tune, "Garry Owen."

The victory was welcomed all over the country, but it had been costly. Captain Hamilton had been killed in the first moment of the attack, there were many wounded, and Major Elliott, with fifteen men, was missing and presumed to be dead.

There was also loud criticism from humanitarians in the East against Sheridan's and Custer's ruthlessness, for the head of the village had been Black Kettle, a chief who had often proved himself friendly to white men. The soldiers had no doubts of the hostility of the village, however, for they had discovered in the tepees bits of finery, bedding and daguerreotypes that proved to have come from homes destroyed in the raids, and also dispatches carried by one of Sheridan's couriers whom the Indians had killed. What was more convincing to them, the troopers had found the recently slain bodies of a white woman and child, evidently prisoners, and had seen an Indian squaw actually stab a small captive white boy before their eyes rather than allow him to be rescued.

Libbie read the charges in the Eastern papers with astonishment and anger. "No one who knew Armstrong as I know him could call him ruthless or cruel!" she declared. "He only did what he had been ordered to do!"

Most horrifying of all to her were the insinuations by some of the Seventh's own officers, sent back by letter, that Custer had made only slight efforts to find Major Elliott and his men and had marched away, leaving them to their fate. Most of the rumors came from Captain Benteen, who later put his criticisms into an anonymous letter to a newspaper. He had always disliked Custer and now his hostility was open and bitter.

Custer, however, stated firmly that he had done his best to find the missing men. Only concern for the safety of his whole command, threatened by a gathering of warriors from many villages farther along the river, had halted his search, he declared, and Sheridan believed him.

Libbie read her husband's jubilant letters about the Washita Battle and felt her hopes rise. Surely this success would bring him back soon! There was still work for the cavalry, however. The other Indians, the Kiowas, Arapahoes and Comanches who had been encamped along the Washita had fled and scattered, and Sheridan was determined that they should be pursued and made to return to the reservations around Fort Cobb and the newly established Fort Sill. By swift forced marches through the biting cold and snow, the soldiers caught up with the largest of the groups under the famous Kiowa chief, Santanta, managed to capture him and, by using him as a hostage, persuaded his people to return and settle down.

One large village of Cheyennes, known to be holding two white girls captive, still evaded the troops. In January Sheridan sent Custer after them with the Seventh and an added body of

Kansas Volunteer soldiers who had enlisted especially to rescue the prisoners. For guides the regiment took two Cheyenne women captured in November on the Washita and who had been won over by friendly treatment. One was Mawissa, sister of Black Kettle, the other Monaseta, daughter of Chief Little Rock, a young and pretty woman with a papoose in a cradle-board on her back.

After a long, hard trek through the empty wilderness they finally located the Cheyenne village, early in March, and sur-rounded it before the Indians could get away. Custer did not attack, for he knew that if he did the captives would be killed without mercy. Instead, with only Lieutenant Cooke beside him, he rode boldly into the Cheyenne village and demanded to speak to their chief. Stone Forehead, the leader, invited them into his tepee for a council of warriors and wise men. They talked in the deliberate Indian manner for several hours, Custer using the sign language he had studied.

When Custer demanded the release of the white captives, Stone Forehead denied any knowledge of them and launched, instead, into another long oration about his exploits in war and his love for the white men. Next, a medicine man went through an elaborate ceremony which, Custer learned later, was magic, supposed to strike him dead on the spot. When it did not succeed he was allowed to leave, still with great expressions of friendship.

The next day three chiefs returned his visit, bringing singers and dancers to entertain him. "They plan for the village to slip away while you are watching the dancing," Monaseta warned him. "And the white girls are there, hidden in a tepee. I have seen them."

Custer acted swiftly. He had the three chiefs seized and threatened to hang them to the nearest tree if the white women were not returned by noon of the next day. Hanging was a death too shameful for any Indian warrior to face, and, after more long arguments, the girls were brought in before the allotted time passed. The chiefs promised that their village would travel to the reservation at Fort Sill, but Custer held his three hostages to ensure the keeping of their vow.

Armstrong wrote the whole story to Libbie. "When we overtook the village and saw it in our power to annihilate it, my command, from the highest to the lowest, desired bloodshed. The Kansans were especially eager for revenge and could not comprehend my conduct in holding off. However, I succeeded without a fight, and now my most bitter enemies cannot say that I am either bloodthirsty or possess an unworthy ambition."

In the spring of 1869, with all the renegade Indians on the Southern Plains believed to be under control, General Sheridan went East and Armstrong journeyed to Fort Leavenworth with joyful news for Libbie. The Seventh Cavalry was to be in camp at Fort Hays during the whole summer.

"Fort Hays?" Libbie echoed, remembering her harrowing experience there two summers before.

"You'll find it very different now," he assured her. "The post has been rebuilt since the flood that drove you out. Officers' Row is now made of fine, two-story houses with porches and fenced-in yards. However, we shan't be right there, for it will house the Infantry under General Miles. The Seventh will be in camp along Big Creek. I've already picked out a fine location for our own tents."

The site Armstrong had selected was high on the bank of the stream, well above flood line and under the shady branches of a big cottonwood tree. It proved to be the most pleasant and most comfortable summer the regiment had yet spent.

After the strenuous winter campaign, horses and men were given a long, well-earned rest, with only short scouting patrols to occupy them.

In their spare time the troopers built a structure of cottonwood logs and canvas, covered by a huge tarpaulin, which they called their "Opera House." It served for a recreation hall, for minstrel performances, concerts, and dances. Once a week the officers gave a "hop" there, and carriages full of young ladies came out from the Infantry post and the little town to share the fun. No one danced more gaily than Autie or was more sought after as a partner than slender, light-footed Libbie.

Besides countless dogs, the men soon acquired any number of wild animal pets—wolf cubs, young antelopes, raccoons, prairie dogs and even a buffalo calf. Tom Custer managed to collect a dozen rattlesnakes. He mischievously invited friends to his tent and seated them on the lid of the innocent-looking box which housed the reptiles, then roared with laughter at his guests' startled leaps upward when the occupants began to rattle.

That summer brought many visitors from the East. Some of them were high-ranking government officials and Custer staged elk and buffalo hunts in their honor, using the opportunity to give his soldiers a change from the salt pork and stringy government beef. Neither General Miles's recent bride, nor Libbie had ever seen a buffalo hunt and they begged their husbands to take them along.

An ambulance was therefore fitted up for them to ride in, with four strong mules to pull it, a skillful driver, and a detail of well-armed cavalrymen to guard it, for there was always danger from roving bands of young Indian braves. Tom Custer rode alongside and Captain Keogh, the laughing, reckless Irishman, on his strong buckskin mount, Comanche, commanded the ladies' escort.

The gay party started out over the prairie in the cool morning air. The bluest of blue skies arched above them, flawless and clear to the far circle of the horizon. From time to time Armstrong came galloping back from his place in the lead, partly to exchange jokes with the ladies and partly to give his horse, Dandy, a chance to stretch his legs. At his approach, as always, Libbie felt her pulses quicken. Even now, she thought, after five years of marriage, it is still thrilling to see him ride—a superb horseman on a superb, spirited animal!

When the hunters sighted a herd of buffalo at last the ladies were driven to an eminence in the rolling prairie where they could watch the sport well out of harm's way. At first the buffalo looked to Libbie like nothing but dark blots on the horizon, but soon they came nearer and the sound of their running hoofs was like advancing thunder.

"There's Autie!" Libbie cried, jumping up in her excitement. "He's lost his hat, as usual. I can tell him by his yellow hair."

Breathlessly she watched him cut one of the animals out of the herd, urge his horse up beside the creature at a dead run and aim his weapon. They were too far away to hear the report of the rifle, but she saw the bison stumble, then fall to its knees and lie motionless on the ground. Libbie closed her eyes for a moment. Killing any free wild creature always sickened her a little, no matter how hard she tried to share the thrill of the chase. And the men *do* need the meat, she said to herself, angry at the qualms which seemed to her somehow disloyal to Armstrong.

Not far from Fort Hays stood a stockade where the Cheyenne women and children, captured on the Washita, and the three chiefs taken later, were housed. They were held there as hostages by the Army until the rest of the tribe fulfilled its promise and returned to the reservation. Custer. visited them regularly. He felt himself responsible for their safety since it was he who had made the bargain with them. He had learned enough of their sign language so that, with some help from an interpreter, he could converse with them freely.

"You'd better go along with Autie, next time," Tom Custer told Libbie one morning. "He walks right into the stockade and you should see how all the squaws come crowding around him, patting him and stroking his hair and rubbing their cheeks against his!"

"Don't worry, Mrs. Custer, it's only the ugly old ones who do that," Captain Keogh assured her. "The pretty young girls stay off by themselves, more's the pity."

"One of them's going to have a knife under her blanket some day, Autie," Tom chuckled. "That yellow top-knot of yours must be mighty tempting to them!"

"Nonsense!" Armstrong declared. "They know I'm the best friend they've got around here. I think you really should come, though, Libbie. After all, it's something to have sixty Indians from a warlike tribe near enough to get acquainted with."

The log stockade was large and there was a sentinel's walk all around it. "I can see them all very well from up there. Do I have to go inside, Autie?" Libbie faltered.

"Certainly. I sent word that you were coming and they want to meet the white chief's squaw. Come along."

As soon as Libbie was inside, the women and children came thronging around her, talking excitedly. "Smile, Libbie. They want to be friendly," Armstrong directed.

After a short moment of staring, two or three of the oldest squaws came close to her. One reached out a claw-like hand and felt the material of her riding habit while another began to probe her grimy fingers into the hair knotted at the back of Libbie's head. Since her earliest childhood-nightmares Libbie had been terrified of Indians, and she could not share Autie's interest and genuine liking for them. With a supreme effort she fought down a shudder and managed a feeble smile, and at the sight they burst into delighted laughter. More and more joined the group until she was closely surrounded. Most of the old women were incredibly ugly, with seamed, wrinkled faces and straggling gray hair. Like the most horrible caricatures of witches, Libbie thought. But they do appear to be friendly, poor things.

Some small children came pushing through the crowd and they, at least, were charming as they touched the bright brass buttons on her riding-habit and stroked the leather of her gloves in wondering admiration at its softness. A young woman brought a baby on a cradleboard to show proudly, and it was easy to admire the swathed little creature with its round, dimpled face and bright black eyes.

Libbie visited the hostages many times after that and once she brought Eliza along. The Indian women were openly astonished over her color. They rolled up her sleeves to see if she were the same hue under her clothing and patted her hair, so different from their own straight locks. Eliza endured it all until she found herself alone in their midst. Panic-stricken, she bolted for the gate, followed by the laughter and hand-clapping of the old women who were pleased and amused to find the "black squaw" afraid of them.

Later that season Custer was summoned hurriedly to the stockade. He arrived to learn that there had been a disastrous fight between the Infantry guards and the Indian prisoners. Rumors had reached the Post that a band of hostiles had left the reservation for the purpose of rescuing the hostages, and the officers decided to put the three chiefs for safekeeping into the guard house. No one could make the Indians understand what was wanted, however, and they became convinced that they were to be hanged. They resisted desperately and the squaws joined the fray, using knives long concealed under their blankets. In the struggle two of the Indian men were mortally wounded by soldiers' bayonets.

When Custer arrived the whole camp of Indians was in an uproar. He went alone into the stockade and, by patient explanations, managed to quiet them. "If I had been sent for in the first place I could have made them understand what we were trying to do!" he fumed to Libbie, on his return. "News of this will travel all over the Plains and the Indians will consider it another breach of faith by the white men. As indeed it *is!*"

Nevertheless, the rest of the Cheyennes returned at last to their reservation and the hostages were sent off to join them. The squaws had become friendly again, but the lone warrior, Fat Bear, showed his bitter hatred in every glance he gave the blue-clad soldiers, as he stalked to his place in the transport wagons.

When fall came the regiment went into winter quarters at Fort Leavenworth. It was a large, well-built post and life there was gay and easy. There were all sorts of festivities to pass the time—hops, concerts, amateur theatricals, horse races, even a hilarious "slow mule race" in which Custer and several other higher officers competed, to the delight of the enlisted men.

During the following summer the regiment was again encamped on Big Creek, then went once more to Fort Leavenworth in the autumn. Custer was able to get leave that winter and he and Libbie returned to Monroe. He left her there among her friends and traveled on to New York with a bear cub for the Zoological Society. His articles on the Western Plains had attracted much notice, and now his letters to Libbie were full of the attentions showered upon him. He wrote of a banquet where, as a successful author, he had sat between Horace Greeley and Bayard Taylor, while Whitelaw Reid, Charles Dana and E. C. Stedman also were at the table.

He saw Lawrence Barrett in his latest play, made friends with a talented and popular singer, Clara Louise Kellogg, and was entertained by the wealthy Jerome brothers, Larry and Leonard, at the races at Saratoga.

The long leave ended in September, 1871, and Custer was ordered to report to Elizabethtown, Kentucky. For once he received news to return to duty without enthusiasm. The Seventh Cavalry was to be distributed by squadron and company over seven Southern states, and their task would be to enforce Federal taxes on distilleries and to suppress the Ku Klux Klan, work for which he had no relish. "It's a job for police," he told Libbie. "After a taste of life on the Plains, everywhere else seems insipid and tame."

From Elizabethtown Libbie wrote to her aunt, "This is the stillest, dullest place!" They had settled down in a small brick cottage connected with a boarding house where they took their meals. The dining room was presided over by the elderly landlady. A contraption made of pieces of boards, ropes and pulleys ran the length of the table, and when it was worked by a small colored boy, a red rag hanging from it fluttered and served to keep the endlessly buzzing flies off the food.

Libbie made the cottage homelike by decorating the walls with pictures and Armstrong's hunting trophies, but she could sense his restlessness at the humdrum existence in the small, dusty town. His chief duties turned out to be the inspection and purchase of mounts for the Army. Libbie encouraged him to do more writing, for the publishers asked for all he could send them, and that work helped him to pass the time.

While he was away on his horse-buying trips, she launched into dressmaking on a newfangled "sewing machine" Autie had bought her. She even experimented on some underwear for Brother Tom. His letter thanking her showed that she still had much to learn. "The drawers are better than the first pair, but you didn't make the strap so it wouldn't twist the leg halfway round. The nighties are very nice, but don't put so much lace on them. Ruffles are better. Make the buttonholes run up and down instead of crosswise. Don't think I'm finding fault. I showed them to Doc and Lt. French and they think they are grand."

In January, 1873, a telegram from Sheridan sent Armstrong's spirits soaring. He was ordered to join a hunting party which the President had arranged for the Grand Duke Alexis, third son of the Czar of Russia. Sheridan would be there and the hunt would be in charge of "Buffalo Bill" Cody, Sheridan's former dispatch rider. Cody had persuaded Spotted Tail, a temporarily friendly Sioux chief, to bring his village along to add to the picturesque effect.

Out came Armstrong's rifles, his fringed buckskins and his winter woollens and he was off. Libbie was invited to join the Imperial party after the hunt, to chaperone two young ladies, Miss Nina Sturgis and Miss Duncan. They would travel by special Pullman down to New Orleans. It would be very gay, with balls and receptions all along the way. "I must have some new clothes," Libbie said, and set to work.

The hunt was a great success. The nineteen-year-old Grand

Duke was an expert rider and a good shot and he plainly enjoyed this part of his trip far more than the series of official receptions he had attended across the country. When he had
brought down his first of eight buffalo he insisted upon cabling
the wonderful news to the Czar, his father. He visited Spotted
Tail in his camp, watched the braves in a war dance, and complimented the Chief's pretty young daughter. For a climax,
Buffalo Bill drove the royal guest and Custer in a stagecoach at
breakneck speed across the prairie.

Libbie met the party at Louisville, where a grand ball was
held in the Prince's honor. Although officially the chaperone,
Libbie was described by a Louisville paper as "a dark loveliness," and her soft voice and graceful dancing charmed the
Grand Duke and all his entourage.

She found the royal youth a large, cheerful, good-looking
young man who listened dutifully to his tutor's coaching on
American history, geography, and politics, but much preferred
dancing, talking with pretty young ladies or joking with Custer
over incidents of the hunt. He had a fine singing voice and had
learned some American music hall ballads. His favorite of all
began "If ever I cease to love" which he rendered with much
sentimental feeling.

At the Duke's special request formality was banished during
the trip. Alexis went in to dinner first with one of the ladies of
the party—a different one each time—and left the table first.
Other than that, no ceremony was observed.

"What a luxurious existence!" Libbie exclaimed, as the morning coffee and rolls were brought to them in their stateroom.
"Imagine, we don't have to rise until noon unless we wish."

The glamorous interlude lasted only until they reached New
Orleans. Then they returned to the dust, flies and dullness of
Elizabethtown again. "I feel like Cinderella after the ball,"

Libbie said, as she packed her pretty gowns away. "Except that I still have my prince with me," she added, with a quick smile for Autie.

In February of 1873, after almost two years of duty at Elizabethtown, Custer received new orders. These he greeted with his old, boisterous joy. "The Seventh Cavalry is to be reunited and sent to the Dakota Territory!" he cried, swinging Libbie high. "Back to the plains again!"

CHAPTER

14

As soon as she was set on her feet again Libbie ran to get the atlas. "The Dakota Territory!" she exclaimed. "How far from everything and how empty it looks! Just where in the territory will the regiment be stationed?"

"At Fort Rice, on the Missouri River," Armstrong said. "The Northern Pacific Railroad is trying to survey a route across to the Yellowstone River, and the Sioux have been giving them trouble. The Seventh's job will be to protect the engineers against them."

Libbie felt a small, cold shudder touch her spine. "Oh, Autie, I've heard that the—the Sioux are the fiercest of all the Plains' tribes," she said.

"Yes, they're good fighting men," he answered. "But they haven't met the Seventh Cavalry yet, Libbie. Don't worry. We'll be able to handle them."

Late in March of 1873 the regiment assembled at Memphis, Tennessee, to board the steamers which would carry them northward. It was a jubilant reunion for the long-separated comrades. Tom Custer, Yates, Keogh, Cooke, Godfrey, Var-

num, Moylan, all were there to greet the Custers, as was handsome young Lieutenant James Calhoun, now wed to Autie's
young sister, Maggie, who would accompany her husband to
his new post. One valued member of the party was absent, however. Eliza was now happily married to a prosperous Ohio
lawyer, and in her place was a new colored couple, Mary and
Ham.

Memphis was warm with spring and the ladies wore light
summer muslins for the start of their journey. The balmy
weather continued as the Seventh traveled up the river to Cairo,
Illinois, then changed to the railroad cars. Slowed down by frequent stops to water and exercise the horses, the trains chugged
northward to where the rails ended at Yankton, just inside the
Dakota Territory.

Libbie was lifted down the high steps of the Pullman car to
the bare, hard-packed earth. Close to the tracks she saw the
familiar confusion of hurrying, shouting men and nervous
horses as the troopers detrained their mounts. Beyond lay a vast,
silent, treeless sweep of short grass and an enormous expanse
of sky, surrounding and engulfing them all. At some distance
down the tracks was the small cluster of houses that was
Yankton.

"Most of the ladies of the regiment are going into town to
the hotel, Libbie. Would you like to go there too?" Armstrong
asked, pausing beside her while his orderly brought up his
horse.

Libbie drew a deep breath of the wine-like air. "No, I think
I'd rather sleep in a tent after so long on that stuffy train.
Mary and I'll stay here until they set up our camp."

Custer rode off with his aides to supervise the laying out of
the camp and Libbie and Mary seated themselves on a chest in
the midst of a stockade of their boxed belongings. Suddenly

Libbie was conscious of a sharp chill in the wind and at once a misty rain began to fall. Not far from the rails stood a small, unfinished cabin and Libbie and Mary hurried to take shelter there while Ham and a few troopers brought in their baggage.

The wind blew harder and the cold increased. Almost before they were inside the structure clouds of snow came whirling in sheets of smothering whiteness. Why doesn't Autie come back? Libbie asked herself anxiously. Out in this storm in light summer clothing! He'll be frozen to death, and the whole regiment with him.

Dusk had fallen by the time Custer appeared at last, for he would not take cover until he had settled his men and horses in the town. He was shaking with chill as he dismounted and his orderly had to help him into the cabin, where he collapsed into unconsciousness.

"He's on fire with a fever!" Mary cried. The hastily summoned doctor pronounced him seriously ill and gave Libbie a phial of drops for him to take every hour, then hurried away to attend other stricken men.

Night came on swiftly while the storm increased to a roaring blizzard which shook the walls and windows as though it would carry the house away. Snow drifted in through the cracks and lay in furrows on the floor. Ham, useless from the first, had long ago disappeared under a pile of bedding, and only Libbie and Mary were left to care for a desperately sick man without food or heat, for there was no stove and no possibility of a fire.

"Oh, Miss Libbie, whatever's going to become of us?" Mary moaned. "The snow's up to the windows already and nobody can get through to help us. I think the General's going to die for sure and the rest of us will just freeze to icicles!"

"Nonsense!" Libbie said sharply. "We may not have heat

but we have plenty of clothing and blankets in our baggage. Unpack the trunks and the bedding. We'll put on all our warmest things and cover him and ourselves with blankets. There's the lantern too. At least we can have light and a little warmth from it."

In spite of her confident words, the next thirty-six hours were a waking nightmare for Libbie. She dared not allow herself to fall asleep, for she must give Armstrong his medicine every hour. Armstrong? Was this helpless, muttering stranger really her husband, always until now her bulwark of strength and courage? Bleak, utter loneliness swept over her, then stark panic. Am I going to lose him now—not in some faroff battle but here, before my own eyes? "No!" she cried aloud and began to beat her numb hands together to force circulation into them so that she could measure his medicine more accurately.

To give him those hourly doses with fingers almost too cold to hold the spoon and to keep him covered, seemed truly beyond her power. "But I must. I *will!*" she whispered each time, and set herself grimly to the task.

The hours dragged on. The blizzard howled without letup. In the middle of the night came a wild pounding on the door. Had help come at last? Mary roused herself to open it and admitted six stumbling, half-frozen soldiers, lost in the storm, who had seen their light and struggled here for shelter.

But how to keep them from freezing, even now? Libbie looked about the shadowy cabin, then her eyes caught a roll of carpets lying in the corner. "Cut the ropes and unroll those rugs. You can cover yourselves with them and if you huddle close together you'll give each other warmth," she directed.

Some of the men had badly frozen hands and feet, and during lulls in the roaring of the wind came the sound of the poor fellows' groans as the painful thawing began. There were other

sounds too. From time to time a lost herd of mules rushed past
in the darkness, driven to frenzy by the storm. Once a drove
of hogs came squealing and grunting against a wall and seemed
to rock the building with their sudden weight. Another thud
on the door? Was it a lost soldier? The door was opened to re-
veal the long face and strange, wild, rolling eyes of a horse. It
peered in for a moment, then, with a snort, was gone into the
wall of whiteness.

All night and most of the next day the blizzard continued,
but at last the wind died down and the sky cleared. The doctor
and other officers fought their way through the drifts to the
beleaguered cabin, where, by this time, Custer's fever had left
him. The arrival of a small, sheet-iron stove, complete with
stovepipe and fuel, soon had the cabin blessedly warm. Hot
food, together with news that the rest of the regiment was safe,
brought back Custer's unquenchable spirits, and he was even
able to laugh with masculine indulgence at Libbie who, now
that all danger was past, gave way to tears.

The citizens of Yankton did their best to make up to the
cavalry for the stormy welcome they had received by giving a
ball in their honor. During the days that followed the sun
shone warm and bright, the snow melted away and the regiment
made ready to start the three hundred and fifty mile trek up
the Missouri River.

The Governor of the Territory arrived to review the
troops, then the long march began. The wives of the other officers chose to make the journey by the steamboat which
would carry supplies up the river, but Libbie and Maggie Calhoun rode with their husbands at the head of the regiment.
The horses were lively after their long rest, the weather was
perfect, and the landscape green with spring. They rode over

deep carpets of new grass and wildflowers, where every hoof-
print sent up fresh, delicious odors.

As Armstrong lifted Libbie down from her horse after the
first day's march she looked about her and stretched her arms
wide. What were hardships, blizzards, dangers? "There was
never anyone in all the world so happy!" she declared. "*You*
well, Autie, and Tom and Maggie and her Jim here with us,
and with our own Regiment all around us once again in this
perfect camping spot! What else is there left for me to pray
for? Except—" The last word was whispered and her breath
caught. One prayer had not been granted Libbie Custer, her
prayer to have children. By now, however, she had learned to
accept the fact that it was not to be, and to comfort herself a
little with the knowledge that the care and education of children would doubtless have made necessary even longer separa-
tions from her soldier-husband.

The march took the Seventh Cavalry through the hunting
grounds set apart for some of the Sioux tribes who were at
peace. One of their chiefs, Fool Dog, came to visit the soldiers'
camp. Tall, dignified, with fine, clear-cut features, he invited
the General to return his call. That evening Armstrong, with
Libbie clinging to his arm, walked over to the circle of Indian
tepees. Terrified, as she always was with Indians, but determined to go wherever Autie went, she crept into the council
lodge with him and sat beside him on a buffalo robe while the
assembled elderly braves smoked the peace pipe. Afterwards
they watched naked, painted boys dance in their honor and
listened to the drums and the strange, minor-keyed songs and
chants which were the Indians' music.

Armstrong was silent and thoughtful as they returned under
the brilliant, low-swinging stars. "Did you notice, Libbie, that
there were practically no young men in sight, only boys and

old men and women? Even in these so-called friendly tribes on
this side of the Missouri, I've been told, most of the young
men go off in the spring to the hostiles across the river. There
they join in the raids against us. The scouts have heard them
boasting that they have taken over the hunting grounds of the
Crows also, who have always been our good friends.

"In the fall, when it's time for the Indian agents to distribute
winter supplies—rations, blankets, hunting rifles and ammunition—the young braves come back to their villages and take
their shares with the rest. It's a bad situation."

On June 10, the column arrived at the infantry post of Fort
Rice which was to be the Seventh's headquarters, to find that
there were no accommodations whatever for the wives of the
cavalry officers. Custer and his men would be starting in ten
days on their Yellowstone expedition to be gone all summer.
There was nothing for Libbie and Maggie Calhoun, then, but
to travel by steamer up to Bismarck and thence by train back
to Monroe, with only the memory of their idyllic march with
the Cavalry for comfort.

Custer's letters to Libbie from the Yellowstone Expedition
were long and full of descriptions of the country through which
they traveled. The column was under the command of the Infantry leader, General Stanley, but the Cavalry did the path-
finding. Custer had hired two able scouts, Bloody Knife, an
Arikara Indian, and "Lonesome Charlie" Reynolds, a shy, silent
white man who was famous all over the West for his knowledge
of the land. Custer, too, had displayed real scouting talent.
"Custer luck" his men called it, while the railroad engineers
were frankly amazed at his ability to discover pathways for
them through the most difficult terrain.

When they reached the Yellowstone River they had some
brushes with hostile Sioux Indians, who had gathered in large

numbers to try to halt the advance of the railroad. They proved unable to stand against the charges of the disciplined troopers, however, and the work continued.

The expedition completed its work in the fall of 1873, and Custer wrote joyfully that he had been given command of a large, recently established Army post across the Missouri River from Bismarck in the Dakota Territory. He hurried to Monroe to bring Libbie, Maggie Calhoun, and their young friend, Agnes Bates, back with him to Fort Abraham Lincoln, as the new post was named. They left the train at Bismarck, crossed the turbulent Missouri partly on the ice, partly in a frail, tossing rowboat, and were met on the other shore by Tom Custer with an army sleigh.

As they drove through the gateway of the post they were met by the strains of "Home Sweet Home" and then "Garry Owen" from the regimental band. Every room in their spacious new quarters was brilliantly lighted, there were fires in all the fireplaces, the house was full of their friends and Mary had a fine supper waiting for them.

"The Seventh Cavalry has a post, a home of its very own at last, Libbie," Armstrong said. "We'll be here for a long stay, they tell me. This is by far the finest house we've ever had, large enough for all the entertaining I'm expected to do as commanding officer. Wait until you see the big wardrobes in our room. No more hanging all our clothes on a few nails in the wall! I tried to get everything ready and settled for you, but you can make any changes you like, of course, darling."

"It's beautiful!" Libbie's eyes were sparkling. "Oh Autie, it's really beautiful."

In the weeks that followed Libbie worked happily at making curtains and arranging furniture in her new domain. Then, in the midst of a cold, still, February night she was awakened by a roaring in the chimney of their room. The house was on fire!

The aroused garrison did what it could, but the building quickly burned to the ground. Only the lack of wind prevented the flames from consuming the whole post. They were fortunate to have escaped with their lives, for little of the house's contents was saved. Pretty Agnes Bates lost every bit of her clothing except her nightdress and one party gown carried out in an otherwise empty trunk.

The terror of the fire and her own flight over the snow to the shelter of the Calhoun's quarters left Libbie in a state of nervous shock. She could not even look at the ruins or the scanty, scorched heap of their belongings piled forlornly on the parade ground without collapsing into tears.

"Don't go near the place, darling, or think about getting settled anywhere else until you feel better," Armstrong told her. "Stay here with Maggie and rest. Everything else can wait until you get your strength back."

The problem of reclothing poor Agnes was solved by the other ladies of the garrison. The very next morning a basket full of garments arrived. Every woman had contributed something of her own and, what was more, arrived soon after with scissors, thimble, needles and thread, ready to remake the garments to fit the girl's figure. Tom Custer volunteered to run the sewing machine and pedaled it manfully with his big, booted foot until a trumpet-call, summoning him back to duty, sent him out of the door at a run, buckling on his sabre as he went.

By the second day after the fire Libbie felt ready to cope with the problem of establishing them in the new quarters on officers' row. "I'll come over this afternoon from headquarters as soon as my work's done and meet you there. We can go through the place and make decisions together," Armstrong told her. But when Libbie arrived it was to find the house warm and bright, fully furnished and ready to move into. Full of their friends also, for a housewarming party was already in progress.

"May I have the first dance?" Autie asked. The band struck up a lively waltz and they whirled away together.

The rest of the winter moved past slowly. Armstrong worked on his writing for which there was now an eager market. There were the weekly "hops," concerts, shows, sleighrides and gatherings every evening for music or companionship to help the closely knit group beguile the long, freezing months of their isolation.

The large parlor of the commanding officer's house was open every evening for visitors, but Custer, busy with his writing, left most of the entertaining to Libbie. She had learned long ago to greet everyone with equal warmth and gracious charm. Day after day, evening after evening, she listened sympathetically and tried to give comfort and advice. Sometimes it was a senior officer with pent-up grievances over injustice from the War Department, sometimes a homesick young lieutenant sighing over the picture of his faraway sweetheart, sometimes an inexperienced young bride tearful from trying to cope with the discomforts and inconveniences of frontier life. Often it was a worried mother with sick children, or at intervals the wife of a brutal, drunken soldier who had fled out into the cold from her husband's violence to the only sure refuge she knew.

Two things Armstrong demanded and insisted upon from Libbie. She must never take part in criticism or gossip concerning any officer or lady of their post. "I'll be your safety valve. If you have anything to say against anyone, please say it to me."

His other "order" was that she leave all domestic work to Ham and Mary and the two younger housemaids whom Mary had brought from the South. "It's enough for you to be out here sharing my danger and hardships," he told her. "Stay out of the kitchen! I'd rather see a rested, smiling face across from me than the finest soufflé in the world on the table."

"You really spoil me shamefully," Libbie laughed, but her eyes were soft as she looked at him. "I've never so much as buttoned my own shoes when you were there to do it for me, have I? And no wonder I enjoy my own parties, when I have none of the worry or care of getting ready for them! Surely, too, there's no greater luxury in life than to have you warm my clothes for me at the fire, these cold winter mornings."

Winter finally passed, the days grew longer, the ice in the Missouri broke up and went out with a thundering roar, and spring began. This year, at least, Libbie was able to welcome the spring without misgivings, for the Seventh was not planning a summer campaign against the Indians. Instead, it was ordered to ride out on an exploring expedition into a region known as the Black Hills, together with two companies of infantry and a group of scientific experts. Boston Custer, a younger brother, had come West for the summer and would ride with the Regiment, and best of all, Libbie herself was to be taken along.

She was already packing her things when word came that, because of the hostility of the Sioux to this violation of what they regarded as their sacred mountains, no women would be allowed to go. Disappointed and rebellious, she watched the too-familiar sight of the long blue column winding away across the undulating green landscape.

After so many such partings, why, oh why do they never become easier? Surely by now I should have some words of comfort for these other women, these young brides like Maggie Calhoun, who are facing it for the first time, she told herself.

It was no use—no brave words would come. All that she could think of was that Autie was going once again out into danger and that she was left behind. Ashamed of her cowardice but still powerless to do anything about it, she hurried into her bedroom and shut the door behind her.

CHAPTER

15

The northern summer came on with a rush, as though it were trying to make up for its shortness by sudden, fierce heat, and with the hot weather came myriads of mosquitoes. Those on the Red River of Louisiana and Texas had been bad enough, but these were twice as ravenous and persistent. Armstrong had had a wide porch built on the front of their quarters in the hope that Libbie could take pleasure there during the long, balmy evenings, but the first onslaught of the mosquitoes drove her indoors.

"It's unbearable to give up using our porch after all the trouble Autie took to have it built," she declared to Maggie Calhoun. Screening the porch with the flimsy cotton netting available was out of the question, so Libbie devised a costume for herself that would foil the buzzing marauders. She wrapped newspapers around her ankles before drawing on her stockings, and made a bag of tarlatan gauze with a drawstring at one end to tie it closely around her neck and with little hoops of rattan to hold it away from her face. Then, tucking her skirts and a shawl around her, she seated herself in her rocker on the porch and defied her tiny enemies.

At first sight of her sister-in-law's fantastic garb, Maggie burst into hilarious laughter, but she was glad to copy her example, and the other ladies followed. Visitors who were introduced to the wives of the Seventh Cavalry's officers gathered in the evenings on the Custers' porch found their appearance startling at first, but after one encounter with Dakota mosquitoes, agreed in admiring their ingenuity.

The Arikara Indian scouts brought mail from the Black Hills Expedition three times during that summer, and Libbie, as always, lived for those letters. Armstrong described the country through which they rode as picturesque and beautiful, with plenty of water, rich grass and heavy timber. The scientists had found interesting fossils and even precious metals, including gold! Custer reported that he himself was obeying Libbie, his "commanding officer," by not riding off by himself even when hunting. Reading this, she smiled and drew a deep breath of relief.

Another letter told of his reaching the highest rung on a hunter's ladder of achievement—he had killed his first grizzly bear. In spite of the threats of the hostile Sioux chief, Sitting Bull, against this invasion of their sacred mountains, the expedition had not been attacked. They had been harassed, however, by the Sioux's setting fire to the prairie grass ahead of them, which had made necessary longer marches than were comfortable in order to reach grazing for the stock. "But I'm an old hand at forced marches," Custer commented. The horses, the men, and the beef herd which supplied their meat were all in better condition than when they had left the fort.

On the afternoon of August 30, the Black Hills column returned and marched jauntily into Fort Lincoln behind their band. The instruments were battered and tarnished, but "Garry Owen" had never sounded more gallant. Uniforms were faded and threadbare, many of the men, including Armstrong, were heavily bearded as well as sunburnt, but they were all cheerful and hearty. When at last her husband jumped from his saddle to the ground at their door and caught her up in a hug worthy of his grizzly bear, the bliss of reunion made up to Libbie for the long weeks of anxiety.

That autumn Custer was given a short leave. *My Life on the Plains*, a collection of his articles for *Galaxy Magazine*, had just been published, and while visiting Chicago Libbie and Armstrong rejoiced to see it in book form at last. In Monroe they picked up Emma Reed, Armstrong's young niece, who was to spend the winter with them. They went next to St. Paul, where he purchased a grand piano for their parlor, and finally back to Fort Lincoln again.

The second Dakota winter was easier and more pleasant than the first. By this time most of the officers of the regiment were either comrades of long standing or relatives of the Custers. Tom Custer and James Calhoun were his brother and brother-in-law, Captain Yates had been Autie's friend since Civil War days, while others, like Moylan, Keogh and Smith had served with him almost as long. Custer loved having this noisy, boisterous group around him, but, in the midst of her enjoyment, the closeness of their circle troubled Libbie, for she knew that there was criticism of it. She did her best to draw others into it, and she had learned to be unflinchingly cordial even to Captain Benteen and Major Reno, although she knew that the former often made sarcastic comments about the newspaper praise and publicity which seemed to follow Custer's every move.

Other matters more important than small dissatisfactions

among the officers were occupying Custer. The Sioux were continuing their raids. Large numbers of them, led by Sitting Bull, still refused point blank to occupy the reservations set apart for them west of the Little Missouri. They made constant attacks on stagecoaches, settlers and travelers, and they had all but driven the peaceful and friendly Crows from the hunting grounds south of the Yellowstone and west of the Rosebud rivers, which had been assigned to them by treaty.

"Are the white soldiers afraid of the Sioux?" the Crow chiefs demanded of their agents. "What use is it to us to be your friends if you do not help us against our enemies?"

Besides this, there was growing evidence that employees of the Indian Bureau were selling modern rifles and ammunition to warriors who, if not themselves openly hostile, were known to be in close touch with Sitting Bull's band. Finally, the sutlers of the army posts, formerly under the control of the commanders of the forts, were now made political appointees and at once began to gather huge and notorious profits. The military were forbidden to deal with anyone else, yet the prices they charged were far above what the same articles could be bought for elsewhere.

"Why don't you report these things to Washington, Autie?" Libbie asked, when he returned fuming from an encounter with one of them.

"I'm forbidden to report to anyone except my superiors in the War Department," Armstrong answered. "And that's exactly where this man sends a big percentage of his gains. Secretary Belknap himself is involved, I've been told, and there's no way to get the information past him."

In January of 1875 Charlie Reynolds, the shy, silent scout who had accompanied Custer on his last two expeditions, came riding in through the snow to see him. "I was at Standing Rock

Agency a while ago, and I heard an Indian boast that it was he who killed those two civilians, Dr. Holzinger and Mr. Baliran, on the Yellowstone two summers ago," he reported. "The other braves all agreed that he should have the credit."

"Who was he?" Custer asked.

"Rain-in-the-Face," Reynolds told him. "He's only a minor chief, but his brother is Iron Horse, one of the leaders of the Uncpapa Sioux. It won't be easy to catch him if he knows you're after him, General."

"Well, we'll have to get him," Custer stated. "We can't have him boasting openly like that. We'll have to make an example of him that will impress the others."

He therefore dispatched Captain Yates and Tom Custer with a hundred troopers on an errand, presumably to Fort Rice. They carried sealed orders, however, which they did not open until they were some distance out on the trail. Without warning they changed their direction and rode swiftly to Standing Rock, where they arrived on the day that the Indians were drawing their rations of beef.

Tom Custer, with five picked men, entered the agency store and lounged about the counter, laughing and talking, until he learned which of the blanketed Indians was the man they sought. Then Tom came up behind him, suddenly pinioned his arms and had him in custody and away before his friends realized what was happening.

They hurried him back to Fort Lincoln and soon his brother, the famous Iron Horse, with many other Uncpapa chiefs, arrived to plead for their young comrade. When they learned that he would have to stand trial for his crime, they presented him with fine robes and ornaments to give him dignity for his ordeal, said sad and formal farewells, and rode away.

Rain-in-the-Face was kept chained in the guardhouse with

some white prisoners, but somehow the agile Indian managed to free himself and to escape. Before he left he vowed revenge on the white soldiers and especially on Tom Custer. "Tell the brother of the Long Hair chief that some day I will meet him in battle. I will cut the heart from his body and eat it while it is still beating!"

Tom laughed the threat off carelessly, but it lingered in Libbie's mind for months. She found herself having the same hideous nightmares of the Raisin River Massacre as had troubled her sleep when she was a little girl. She did not mention them to Armstrong, however, for she felt ashamed of such vague, childish terrors when he was facing dangerous realities.

Early cold had frozen the river, and the steamer sent with supplies to the agency Indians had been caught in the ice and held in the channel all winter. Food ran low on the reservation and the Indian leaders came to Fort Lincoln to ask Custer's help, for their agent could do nothing for them. Their chief orator, Running Antelope, wrapped his blanket around him like a Roman toga and made an eloquent speech describing the sufferings of his people, punctuated by the Indians' graceful, sweeping gestures. He added a denunciation of the agent who, he said, had actually taken some of the supplies off the steamer but had sold them for his own profit instead of distributing them to the people under his care.

Custer knew only too well that this was true. He telegraphed at once to the War Department to ask permission to give some of the plentiful supplies in the fort storehouses to the Indians to tide them over until spring. The answer came back at once from the Secretary of War himself. It was a refusal. The reason was that it would "involve complexities with the Department of the Interior," under which the Indian agents functioned.

This, of course, was impossible to explain to the hungry Indians and they went away bewildered and bitterly angry.

Custer was as angry as any of them. "If I were an Indian, you may be sure that I should take my chances out on the plains, even join the hostiles, rather than starve to death at an agency," he told Libbie, his blue eyes blazing.

Winter passed, spring came again. News that the Black Hills Expedition had found gold had spread through the country, and fortune hunters swarmed into the region in spite of the government's warnings that it was still, by treaty, Indian land. The Sioux were savage in their attacks on the invaders of their sacred mountains, while the Indian agents issued futile orders for the miners to keep out of the territory and for the Indians to stay near the agencies and to refrain from violence. Although they seemed powerless to control their charges, they still clung jealously to their semblance of authority and to the "peace policy" which they were now following. The army was forbidden to go out on any more punitive raids.

Bickering between the Indian Bureau and the War Department filled the newspapers with hints of scandal and corruption in high places. Later in the summer Secretary of War Belknap himself visited Fort Lincoln on a tour of inspection. Custer ordered the regulation salute to his superior, but he did not meet him at the post's boundary nor did he invite him to his home. Instead he waited in his own office and received him there with icy formality.

"Wouldn't it be wise to be a little more politic?" Libbie asked, worried by his manner. "A man in his position can make great difficulties for you, Autie."

"I have given him every courtesy prescribed by military regulations," Armstrong stated. "I respect his office, but I am not required to show personal liking for the man himself when he's a notorious scoundrel!"

With no campaign for the regiment, the summer passed quietly with picnics, rides, and hunting trips. There were more visitors than ever, and most of them wanted above all things to meet the celebrated General Custer, whose book, *My Life on the Plains*, was making such a sensation. Bored by most of these admirers, Armstrong avoided them when he could and left their entertainment to Libbie. At one time he even hid out all day long in a chicken-house rather than subject himself to their stares and questions.

In the fall Custer was given leave, and he and Libbie went to New York for a real "fling" of operas, concerts, and theatres. Lawrence Barrett was appearing as Cassius in *Julius Caesar*, and Armstrong visited him often behind the scenes. Because of the success of *My Life on the Plains*, the publisher was eager to discuss a volume of memoirs. A lecture bureau offered him an engagement at the princely sum of two hundred dollars per evening, five nights a week. "We'll be rich!" he told Libbie, exultantly. "We'll probably have a campaign against the Sioux next summer, but as soon as that's over I can get leave and begin lecturing."

"A campaign against the Sioux?" Libbie echoed, and for a moment a shadow dimmed the brightness of her smile as she listened to his eager plans.

Custer was given several extensions of his leave, and it was February before they journeyed back to the Post. Between St. Paul and Bismarck they ran into a snowstorm. Soon their train was blocked by huge drifts which stalled the locomotive on the track, holding it immobile for several days. Finally a familiar, hallooing shout reached their ears. There was Tom

Custer beside the train with a bobsled drawn by strong army mules!

Libbie was bundled in blankets, carried out through the deep snow and dumped into the straw-filled bed of the sleigh along with Autie's two big stag hounds, who, at least, added a little to her warmth, if not her comfort. It was still snowing when the driver cracked his whip and the mules struggled and floundered off through the drifts. The line of telegraph poles beside the tracks, dimly glimpsed through the whirling flakes, was their only guide across the vast white wilderness. Remembering her other experience in a Dakota blizzard, Libbie hardly dared to believe that they would win through to safety, and it seemed a miraculous answer to prayer when they drew up at last before the door of their own quarters in Fort Lincoln.

They had barely unpacked their belongings when a telegram arrived ordering Custer back to Washington. Libbie began to replace her clothes in the trunk, but Armstrong shook his head. "No, darling, I'm not going to subject you to a winter journey again," he said. "I'll go alone this time. They want me to testify before a Congressional committee that's investigating corruption in the War Department. They won't keep me there long, for I'll be needed here to prepare for our summer campaign against Sitting Bull and his renegade Sioux."

"A summer campaign? It's actually settled?" she whispered, tremulously.

"Yes, it's certain, now," he said. "The agents have finally decided to ask the Army to get the Sioux back on their reservations. They are paid according to the number of Indians at their agencies, so the hordes of warriors who've gone off to join the hostiles have finally hit them where it hurts, in their pocketbooks! We'll have a large, powerful force that should do the job once and for all. General Terry, Commander of the Department, will be coming on from St. Paul to direct the whole thing, General Crook will come up from Wyoming, and General Gibbon from Montana to join us. It will require a lot of work to get the regiment outfitted and ready."

Libbie spent some anxious days after he set off through the snow, but at last a telegram announced his arrival in Washington. Then there were his letters to wait for and the belated newspapers to read in which the progress of the Congressional Investigation was reported in bitter and partisan terms. Although Secretary Belknap hastily resigned to try to escape impeachment, the Senate insisted upon holding hearings anyway. Custer spoke out in his blunt and forthright fashion, but his testimony was dismissed as valueless for "lack of definite proof."

By this time April was half over, yet he was still not released to join his command. Finally he appealed directly to President Grant to allow him to reach his regiment in time to take part in the campaign. The old soldier, resentful of Custer's charges against his cabinet officer, refused even to see him and gave orders that the command of the Seventh Cavalry should be taken from him. This was the worst, most humiliating punishment possible for George Armstrong Custer, and the newspapers at once took up the cause of the popular "Boy General," in blaring headlines.

Back at Fort Lincoln this news was received with astonishment and dismay. Major Reno at once applied for command of the Seventh, while officers and men looked at each other in consternation. "March out without Old Curly?" the troopers whispered, glowering. Even men who disliked Custer's taut discipline felt far more confidence in his fighting leadership than in Reno's.

At last General Terry, who was an able soldier but totally inexperienced in Indian warfare, convinced Grant that the success of the campaign would be in jeopardy without Custer, and the President reversed his decision. Through all these confusing changes, Libbie's heart was torn within her. She knew how hurt her husband would be if he were kept from the campaign—*But he would be safe!* she whispered to herself.

On May 10 Custer arrived with General Terry. He was so boyishly jubilant that Libbie could not but be happy for him. The regiment had already gone into camp a short distance down the river in readiness for the march, and Custer lost no time in joining them. He took Libbie there with the promise that she could go along on the first day, riding with him at the head of the troops as she had done so often before.

On May 17 all was ready. Reveille echoed through the camp at four o'clock in the morning and the soldiers roused themselves in a cold and foggy dawn. The heavy, white-topped wagons were packed and started off first, followed by the beef-herd and the extra mules and horses, moving through thick white mist that hung over the river. The infantry and the field artillery formed ranks and marched out and last of all the cavalry trumpets blared the order to mount. The seasoned troopers swung into their saddles, the band on its gray mounts struck up "Garry Owen." The Seventh Cavalry was on its way!

On the outskirts of the post they passed through the camp of the Arikara scouts, and as the tough little warriors joined the march their squaws and children and old men set up a strange, wailing chant in which the braves joined, beating out the rhythm on the small war drums they carried.

Into Fort Lincoln, then, and across the parade ground the regiment clattered, led by their officers in column of platoons. Flags and guidons were brilliant against the gray mist, spurs and bits jingled, chargers moved on dancing, restless hoofs to the gay tune. Sitting her horse a little behind Armstrong as he reviewed the parade, Libbie watched the men ride past, deeply moved. Surely there was no more stirring sight in all the world! So many friendly, long-familiar faces, some near and dear to her. Charlie Reynolds and Bloody Knife, Custer's favorite scouts; Tom, of course, so like Autie but with a reckless swagger all his own; handsome Jim Calhoun, Major Reno, Captain Benteen—even these two looked competent and brave as they rode past. Captain Cooke with his long black whiskers, young Frank Gibson who had left a pretty bride alone at desolate Fort Rice, George Yates, Autie's oldest friend, Myles Keogh, still riding his durable buckskin mount, Comanche, merry little Benny Hodgson and Jack Sturgis, the youngest officer in the regiment. Smith, Harrington, Godfrey, Weir, Reilly, Crittenden, McIntosh, Porter—so many others!

There was a short halt while the married men said goodbye to their wives and children, then they mounted and moved away again into the mist to the rollicking strains of "The Girl I Left Behind Me." *I hate that tune!* Libbie thought clenching her gloved hand on the reins with sudden passion.

A bright sun had begun to pierce the haze and suddenly, as the long column wound its way into the distance, a mirage appeared. It lifted about half the line of the horsemen, and for an interval they seemed to be marching both on the earth and in the sky. "How beautiful and how strange!" Libbie exclaimed to Maggie Calhoun, waiting beside her. But by the time Armstrong joined them, the apparition had disappeared.

They cantered to the head of the slowly moving column and, that evening, selected a campsite on the bank of a small, clear stream. Armstrong had never been in higher spirits. "Libbie, I can't tell you how good it is to breathe this air after being cooped up for so long in Washington!" he said. "I declare, I'd rather be a trooper out here on these plains than a high-ranking infantry officer anywhere else in the country."

It was an outwardly cheerful family party that camped that night near the soldiers' bivouac. Besides Armstrong and Libbie, Maggie and Jim Calhoun, Tom and Boston Custer, there was also Armstrong Reed, sister Lydia's young son. He had come west for the summer and now was the proud and busy holder of a job helping to drive the beef-herd.

Libbie had never tried harder to keep her fears to herself. She clung desperately to Armstrong's promise that, although she could not march overland across the country with the column, she might come later by one of the supply steamers and join them when they reached the Yellowstone River. "It won't be more than a few weeks before we'll be together again," he assured her.

Nevertheless, when reveille sounded and parting was inevitable, she could barely hide her tears. She blinked them back valiantly and managed a faltering smile as John Burkman, Armstrong's "striker," lifted her to her saddle. "Goodbye, John. You'll look after the General, won't you?" she asked.

"Yes, ma'am, that I will," he promised.

The Custers' farewell was brief. There was too much that might have been said even to attempt speech. They exchanged one steady, clear look, Libbie lifted her horse's rein resolutely and, with Maggie beside her, faced about to ride with their escort back to the Fort. She dared not trust herself to turn her head again.

CHAPTER

16

It was fortunate that the infantry companies left to guard Fort Lincoln were well-officered, for almost at once the post was in a virtual state of siege. Bands of hostile Sioux began to make raids on the outer pickets just before dawn and to try to drive off the beef-herds. The rattle of drums, the "long roll" calling out the soldiers, awakened Libbie night after night. She lay shivering in her bed listening to the gunfire and prey to the fears that were never really absent from her mind, her fears for Autie.

By day she busied herself about the house and penned long, cheerful, newsy letters to be sent by the next courier. If only I could have gone along! she thought.

"We are raising chickens," she wrote to him brightly. "Already we have forty-three. The weather has been hot, but the nights are cool. The light on the hills and valleys is exquisite. The wildflowers are beautiful and so sweet-scented. Em gets bouquets every day. The river is high—too high for any sandbars to show."

At last scouts returned bringing letters from Armstrong.

They told of continuous rain which had muddied the trail and bogged down the wagons so that in the first four days they had made only forty-six miles. No sign of Indians yet, but he was being "extremely prudent" nevertheless, as he had promised her he would be. Tom and he had had fried onions for breakfast and raw onions for lunch. They were taking advantage of her absence to indulge in the vegetables she disliked so much. Tom and Boston played jokes on each other constantly. Next time they went on an expedition like this he'd surely bring Libbie. She could have endured this one as well as not.

The next batch of letters came by steamer, for by this time the column had reached the Yellowstone River at the mouth of the Powder. Custer wrote with boyish pride that General Terry had congratulated him on finding a road through the Badlands when the scouts themselves had lost their way. After riding all day, he told her, he not only wrote to her but he also worked on his *Galaxy* articles, for he had brought his notes along. An article was enclosed in one of the letters with directions for her to read it, then send it on to the publisher.

When the steamer "Far West" docked next at Fort Lincoln, Libbie and Mrs. Smith, the wife of one of the Seventh's officers, went down to the landing. Seeing them, Captain Grant Marsh invited them to come aboard and lunch with him.

"Captain, I must confess that we had a special motive when we came here," Libbie said, with a smile and a sweep of her lashes. "The General has given permission for us to join him at his supply base on the Yellowstone River. We are both good campaigners and we promise to make no trouble for you if you will take us on as passengers."

"Passengers!" the Captain repeated in dismay. "Oh no, ma'am, I couldn't possibly take you aboard as passengers. I have no facilities at all for ladies, and besides, it's far too dangerous.

The Sioux are forever firing on us from the banks and sometimes, going through a narrow channel between high bluffs,
they make it pretty hot for us. I'm sorry, ma'am, but it's
impossible."

Not even the sparkle of tears in Elizabeth Custer's lovely
gray eyes could move the Captain to change his decree, and
the ladies went sadly up the hill and back to their quarters.

One quiet morning the garrison sprang suddenly to life. In
response to a telegraphed dispatch, Indian scouts were fitted out
and sent off at high speed. As soon as they were safely on their
way and secrecy no longer necessary, Libbie learned what had
been in the message.

General Crook's column, coming up from the south to help
entrap the Sioux, had been met on Rosebud Creek by a large
war party under Chief Crazy Horse, had fought to a standstill,
and had been compelled to retreat. Those victorious warriors
were now on their way to join Sitting Bull and add to his
strength with their "good medicine." Because of the hostile
country between the two commands, this news had had to be
sent in this roundabout fashion. Would the Arikara couriers
reach the expedition in time to warn them of the added peril?

After another interval Libbie received more letters from
Armstrong with news that they had located the general where-
abouts of Sitting Bull's village. "I hope to have a good report
to send you by the next mail," Custer wrote. "A success will
start us all toward Lincoln."

On Sunday, June 25, the wives of the officers of the Seventh
gathered in Libbie's parlor to sing old hymns. Why was news
so slow in coming? "They are on a long scout up one of the
rivers," Libbie tried to explain. "It is such difficult country that
even couriers can't get through. We must be calm and patient."

Calm and patient! She herself was all quivering turmoil

within, but, as senior officer's wife, she must not show her fear. She must set an example to all of these women.

July 4th came, and still no news. Far away in Philadelphia, the nation was celebrating the hundredth anniversary of the Declaration of Independence at a great Centennial Exposition. The President and most of the important members of the government were there. At Bismarck, across the river from the fort, there were fireworks and there were special festivities at the post. The enlisted men held wheelbarrow races and contests to catch a greased pig, while in the evening the Infantry gave a ball to which the wives of the Seventh's absent officers were invited. Libbie attended, escorted by one of the officials. Her feet kept time to the music but there was a cold, aching weight just under her heart.

She had learned that a change had come over the camp of the Arikara scouts. They were talking to each other of a great battle and many of them had begun to mourn for the dead. "It's nonsense, of course," an Infantry officer assured her. "They couldn't possibly have any word before we do. Don't let it alarm you, Mrs. Custer."

She nodded and smiled, but her throat was too tight to let her speak. Indians *did* have some special power to send messages swiftly across long distances. Autie had told her that. *Autie!*

On the evening of the fifth the women gathered again in Libbie's parlor, but the songs would not come. Instead they prayed together, then parted for the night. Next day dawned hot and sultry. Early in the morning Libbie heard a knock at the back door. She had been far too restless to go to bed that night and had only taken off her dress. Now she flung on a dressing-gown and hurried out of her room.

Mary met her, her face a strange, gray color. "Miss Libbie,

it's Dr. Middleton and two other officers. They want you and Miss Maggie and Miss Em in the parlor."

The three men seemed to her to have sickened and aged since she saw them last. They looked at her for a moment without speaking, then they broke the news. The Far West had docked the night before, bringing a load of wounded soldiers and an even heavier burden—tidings of disaster. In a battle with overwhelming numbers of Sioux on the Little Big Horn River, five companies of the Seventh Cavalry had been utterly wiped out. Not a man of them was left to tell what had happened. Armstrong, Tom, Jim Calhoun, Boston—even young Autie Reed— all were dead and with them many, many more. The other companies under Reno and Benteen had been pinned down several miles away, and had lost heavily too.

Libbie listened as though she were hearing something long familiar to her. *So it has come at last*, she found herself thinking with a strange, numb calmness. In spite of the heat of the day she began to shiver, but her voice was steady to her ears as she spoke. "You will have to tell the other wives, won't you? I'll come with you and be there with them when they are told. I can do that much for them, at least. But first, will someone fetch me a wrap? It seems to have grown so very cold all of a sudden."

The terrible news broke like a bombshell across a country that was still exulting in its Centennial celebration. Custer had been a national hero during the Civil War and his colorful personality, his exploits in the West, his articles and his lately published book had kept him in the public eye. Most of all, he had been in the middle of a heated political controversy only a few months before, and the enemies of Grant's administration now pounced on the chance to accuse Grant of blame for Custer's death.

To defend himself, Grant struck back by stating that Custer's defeat had been his own fault. He had disobeyed Terry's orders, the President said, had attempted to win the victory all for himself and had brought his regiment to disaster through overweening ambition. Terry himself had implied almost the same thing in one of his first reports.

Libbie had journeyed back to Monroe with Maggie and Em, moving automatically in a daze of shock. These accusations roused her from her frozen grief to look once again at Autie's last letter. "I send you an extract from Terry's official order, knowing how keenly you appreciate words of commendation and confidence in your dear 'Bo' " he had written to her. Then he had quoted the orders, word for word. "It is of course impossible to give you any definite instructions in regard to this movement, and, were it not impossible to do so, the Department Commander places too much confidence in your zeal, energy, and ability to impose on you precise orders which might hamper your action when nearly in contact with the enemy."

Libbie stared at the words with burning eyes. Given such broad leeway in orders plainly set forth in the official records, as they must be, how could anyone say that Armstrong had been disobedient? It was wickedly unjust and unfair to make such accusations when he was no longer here to defend himself!

"But *I* am here," she said aloud, suddenly. She lifted her head and straightened her shoulders in their unrelieved widow's black. "*I* am here," she repeated.

In the midst of her desolation she had found a reason to go on living. Armstrong's memory must be kept untarnished and bright. Like Achilles in the old story, he had died young, but she would make sure that he received his rightful due of all the glory he had won.

She left Monroe, where the surroundings were so painful to her, and moved to New York. Controversy still raged around the battle, but Armstrong's friends were many and they rallied to his defense. A former Civil War comrade, now an editor, called to ask if she would aid him in writing Custer's biography, and no loving widow could have asked for more fulsome praise than Frederick Whittaker gave to her hero.

Most notable and authoritative of Custer's defenders was General Nelson A. Miles. He had been in charge of an official party which visited the battlefield, went over the ground and investigated every report. His research convinced him that criticisms of Custer were unfounded and that Reno and Benteen had been at fault. "It is easy to kick a dead lion," was his terse comment.

In October, 1877, Custer's body was taken from its battlefield grave and reburied at West Point with military honors. The ceremony was an agony for Libbie, but she endured it, buoyed up by concern for Armstrong's father and sister Maggie, who had come from Michigan.

After it was over Libbie returned to New York. It was clear to her that she would have to find some sort of employment, for her insurance and Army pension gave her only a meager income. Of course "ladies" were not supposed to work in those days, but Libbie found a place for herself as the paid secretary of a charitable organization. It was not demanding and it gave her time to answer all the floods of letters that kept pouring in to her.

A purpose had taken shape in her mind and she set to work to achieve it. She was determined to secure an official inquiry into the circumstances of her husband's death which, she was sure, would vindicate him. But how to start the ponderous machinery of the Army on such a task? She persuaded Frederick Whittaker to write to his Congressman and to the newspapers, blasting Major Reno and urging a Congressional investigation. This new publicity helped to goad Reno into demanding, in his own defense, a Military Court of Inquiry.

The inquiry took place in January of 1878, but the verdict pleased no one. It exonerated Reno from blame for the disaster, but in such guarded terms that any sensitive man would have felt disgraced. As for Custer, his enemies whispered that there had been a "gentleman's agreement" among the surviving officers of the Seventh, before the court convened, to withhold criticism of their dead commander out of deference and devotion to Mrs. Custer.

Libbie was far from satisfied, but she was faced with another problem now. Some well-wishers had erected a statue of Custer at West Point which seemed to her a monstrosity, totally unworthy of its subject. She appealed to every authority in turn and finally to General Sherman to have it removed. "I literally cried it off its pedestal," she said later.

By this time Libbie's finances were greatly improved, partly by an increase in her pension and partly from an inheritance, and she was able to give up her job. During these months she had a visit from Eliza, who had traveled all the way from Ohio to see her. The two women laughed and cried in each other's arms as they recalled their life together with the "Ginnel."

After a vacation trip to Europe, Libbie began a new project. She had written literally hundreds of letters during the past five years, for she had answered every one which came to her concerning her husband. Besides all these, she had written to thank writers of articles in the press which praised Custer, and to refute others which criticized him.

Now it occurred to her that she herself might put what seemed to her the truth before his countrymen in permanent form. She could not presume to be a military historian, but she could write from her own memory the story of their life together on the Dakota frontier. *Boots And Saddles*, her account of the Seventh Cavalry at Fort Lincoln, was published in 1885.

Writing it had been difficult for her, for it had stirred up many painful memories, but if it helped even a little to keep Armstrong's name bright, it was worth any cost. The book was a surprising success, and she was able to do more traveling, for a restlessness had come over her as soon as the work was done. Later she wrote a second volume, *Tenting on the Plains*, describing their ride to Texas after the War and life at Fort Riley. In 1890 came *Following the Guidon*, which began with the Battle of the Washita and ended with orders to go to Kentucky. These too were successful. Libbie bought herself a home in New York and also a summer cottage at Oneonta, New York, in a colony of writers and artists.

Many requests came for the author to speak from public platforms all over the country. Libbie was now a celebrity in her own right, but never in her own mind. "It is all for *his* sake," she declared firmly. "Without people's admiration for him, I would be nothing." She no longer wore widow's crepe. "It's too dramatic," she explained. "Although it *is* very becoming."

So the years rolled on. Libbie did more traveling and even circled the globe on one of her trips. In 1910 the State of Michigan erected a fine equestrian statue of General Custer in a public square of Monroe. President Taft came to dedicate it and Libbie, still slender and lovely, with a modish, ostrich-plumed hat on her lustrous dark hair, watched proudly while her eyes brimmed with memories.

In 1926, fifty years after the battle, an anniversary celebration took place on the bare and lonely hills beside the Little Big Horn River. By now the conflict there seemed to have passed into misty legend, like Thermopolae and Roncevalles. A detail of the Seventh Cavalry was sent up from its post in Texas to take part, and descendants of Custer's Crow scouts were there too, as well as sons and grandsons of the Sioux warriors. They went over the battlefield together, looking at the white stones which now marked where each soldier fell and telling one another what they had heard of it from their fathers and grandfathers.

Libbie had been invited, but she declined because of frail health. She was now over eighty, but still erect and soft-voiced and still, when she chose to go out in society, the center of attention from gentlemen of any age. After the semi-centennial ceremonies, letters came to Libbie from all over the country. She answered every one, most of them in her own hand, and all with some special, personal word. Her days were full, her friends surrounded her with warmth and love.

In the spring of 1933, when she was almost ninety-two, Elizabeth Custer died at her home in New York City, quietly secure in the knowledge that her pledge to keep Armstrong's fame burnished and shining had been fulfilled. He had no more enemies left in all the world. She had outlived them all!

Libbie had ridden proudly and joyfully beside her husband at the head of his troops many times. Now, surely, she was as proud and as joyful when, at West Point on April 6, 1933, she was carried by military cortege, moving to the sound of martial music, to where he had lain alone for more than fifty years, waiting for her to join him.

BIBLIOGRAPHY

Elizabeth Custer
  Boots and Saddles, Harper, N.Y., 1885
  Tenting on the Plains, Webster, N.Y., 1889
  Following the Guidon, Harper, N.Y., 1890
George Armstrong Custer
  My Life on the Plains, Quaife, N.Y., 1874
Marguerite Merrington, editor
  The Custer Story, Devin-Adair, N.Y., 1950
Katherine Gibson Fougera
  With Custer's Cavalry, Caxton, Caldwell, Idaho, 1940
Col. W. A. Graham, editor
  The Custer Myth, Stackpole, Harrisburg, Pa., 1953
Edgar I. Stewart
  Custer's Luck, Univ. of Oklahoma Press, Norman, Okla., 1953
Jay Monaghan
  Custer, Little Brown, Boston, 1959
Frazier and Robert Hunt, editors
  I Fought With Custer, Scribners, N.Y., 1947
Glendolin D. Wagner
  Old Neutriment, Boston, 1934
Lt. Col. Melbourne C. Chandler, U.S.A.
  Of Gary Owen in Glory (The history of the 7th U.S. Cavalry),
    Exposition, N.Y., 1960
James M. De Wolf (Editor, Major E. S. Luce)
  Diary and Letters, Reprint from *Montana Magazine*
Charles Kuhlman
  Legend Into History, Stackpole, Harrisburg, Pa., 1952
  Did Custer Disobey Orders? Stackpole, Harrisburg, Pa., 1957
Battles and Leaders of the Civil War (Century War Series), Yoseloff,
  N.Y., 1956

BIBLIOGRAPHY

Henry Steele Commager (editor)
The Blue and the Gray, Bobbs Merrill, Indianapolis, 1950
General Nelson A. Miles
Personal Recollections, Chicago, 1896
General Philip H. Sheridan
Personal Memoirs, N.Y., 1888
George Bird Grinnell
The Fighting Cheyennes, N.Y., 1915
Margaret Leech
Reveille in Washington, Harper, N.Y., 1941